Silence
please!

The Irish Museum of Modern Art, Dublin
Scalo Zurich – Berlin – New York

Stories after the works of
Juan Muñoz

Silence please!

Juan Muñoz
Louise Neri
James Lingwood

Editorial Note
This book began on the occasion of Juan Muñoz's
exhibition at the Irish Museum of Modern Art,
June – August, 1994, curated by James Lingwood.

Assistant Editor: Frances Richard
Designer: Hans Werner Holzwarth, Berlin
Production Coordinator: Roland Läuchli
Production: Steidl, Göttingen

© 1996 for the texts by the authors
© 1996 for the photographs: Irish Museum of Modern
Art, Dublin (p. 10), Kristien Daem (p. 22, 36, 67),
IVAM Centre del Carme, Valencia (p. 45),
Julian Lopez (p. 77, 89, 135), Aideen McConville (p. 99),
Dorothea Fischer (p. 119), Juan Muñoz (p. 160)
© 1996 for this edition:
The Irish Museum of Modern Art, Dublin
and Scalo Zurich – Berlin – New York
Head Office: Weinbergstrasse 22a,
CH-8001 Zurich / Switzerland,
Phone 41 1 261 0910, Fax 41 1 261 9262

Distributed
in North America by D.A.P., New York City;
in Europe and Asia by Thames and Hudson, London

Contents and List of Plates

Introduction

Louise Neri

The initial impulse for this book came to me from an artist and a curator both of whom, like many artists and few curators, are profoundly ambivalent about the closed-off, stillborn nature of much art criticism. They were in the latter stages of planning an exhibition of the artist's work in a spectacular historical site that would counterpose one of the largest and most elaborate conversation pieces ever made with some of the most unsettling and recalcitrant sculptures I've ever met. In the anxious, restless terrain of this artistic œuvre, the always-subjective encounters between sculptures and spectators assume an even more disconcerting proximity. Accordingly, we imagined that a likeness of these experiences might be best rendered in a book of staged contingencies. This book would not only function as a synapsis between the visual and literary image; it would also be "a book among books." As we went on, we learned that what this required was not a form as such, but rather an invitation to invent a form relevant to the idiosyncratic demands of the composition—the composition being the intricate web of affective relationships involved in experiencing a work of art. And thus, surreptitiously, did the notion and structure of fugue, with its unruly contrapuntal dynamic, insert itself as our motivic proposition.

So, we want to write a fugue: Somewhere, an artist makes a sculpture, and then another, each one an embodiment of the skepticism that pervades the loneliness of the studio or the erotic space of the head.

We need an original subjective idea for the fugal structure: Later, somewhere else, the sculpture, cut loose by the artist from the safety of an objective situation, suddenly finds itself exposed to all manner of vicissitudes. There, a shutterbug snaps away, arbitrarily recording the sculpture in its moments of discomfort, curiosity, fear, duplicity, frustration, lostness.

The fugal structure requires events which provide some specific contribution to the original subjective idea. These events will not recur or recombine in precisely the same relationship at any one time: Somewhere else again, prompted by this snapshot evidence, someone begins to tell a story, an episode in which the sculpture is implicated; how and to what degree is of no consequence.

Within the forward movement and consistent density of the fugal structure, each episode must inaugurate its own special problem, its own unique cause for anxiety: Some photos, some stories, which came first now seems unclear and unimportant. But what is important and striking about the protagonists of these stories is their relentless sense of ill-fitting existence. Here, burn-outs, paranoiacs and loners, malcontents and misfits, cheerful or desperate delusionists all are trapped in the callous loops of coincidence, resonance, repetition. Diverting our attention from the silenced figures and emptied scenes of the images, these characters recount to us incidents that seem to have happened many times before, but never in this way, and never in such company. But the images turn their backs or simply pretend not to notice the possible episodes of their lives unfolding. The characters press on with their storytelling. One narrative insinuates itself with another, and the next, and the one after that. And thus develops a rumour of exponential proportions about an artist who bears a startling resemblance to the artist none of us knows.

Ultimately, the fugal composition depends upon the degree to which one can relinquish formulae in the interests of creating form: Fugue's persistent baroque pulse beckons to us from the threshold of this series of oddly related episodes, and its alternative, etymological meaning draws us still further in. For fugue also refers to the state of psychological lapse during which one is said to experience extreme lucidity within a condition of objective amnesia.

And if, indeed, it is the artist's transcendental abilities that we envy and admire, then the art of fugue, which touches the private affective domain of art in its temporary flights from reality, is bound to appeal to the escapist in us all.

Mayflies

Dave Hickey

"I am very free now," he said.

We were sitting on the veranda overlooking the dry lake bed. The angle of the shadow fell across his face so I could only see his lips and chin. They were smooth and well-made. Patrician features, I suppose, expressing no particular sense of strength, nor any sense of weakness, either. He was just a pleasant-looking young man wearing a fresh white linen shirt, pressed black linen slacks and a pair of rubber flip-flops. He sat in a tall rattan chair with his legs crossed, his hands resting in his lap, his head tilted back into the pyramid of shadow.

"I am very free now," he said again, sounding calm as he said it, although I couldn't see his eyes. "I am more free," he said, "than any member of my family in the past four hundred years. Of all those who have gone before me, I am the one most free."

The young man's declaration didn't seem to require a reply, or, at least, I couldn't think of one, so I nodded to acknowledge what he had said. He nodded to acknowledge my acknowledgment and continued.

"For instance," he said, "I used to gamble. I thought that was required of me. So I did it. Now, I can see that

I am too free even for that, and when you are too free even for baccarat, you are extremely free."

"More free than I am," I said.

"Yes, but you are extremely lucky," he said. "And that is a lot better than being extremely free."

I didn't want to discuss it. It seemed to me that he was extremely lucky, too. Lucky to have found a friend when he needed one. I looked off toward the pink mountains.

"They say Coronado marched through here," I said, raising my arm to point, "right through that notch in the mountains, on his way north."

"He must have felt at home," the young man said. "This is a landscape in which I feel at home. It is very old."

"Old," I said. "But not very free."

"Landscapes cannot be free or not-free," he said. "Unless you are political. But it is interesting to think about. Perhaps one of us, one of my family, came riding up through here with Coronado. I do not know for certain. It is not documented, as the connection of my family with Columbus and Velasquez is documented, but it is very likely nevertheless. Wherever there are beans, there will be those to count them. Particularly if they are government beans."

"Bean-counters," I said.

"Bureaucrats," he said, "Civil servants, pirates of the quill. That is the traditional calling of my ancestors."

"My ancestors were shop-keepers," I said.

"Shop-keepers speed things up," he said. "My ancestors devoted their lives to slowing things down, to stately progress that was so stately, it was not, in fact, progress at all. I have one ancestor who devoted his adult life to discrediting Don Diego de Silva Velasquez. Day in and day out, while the great painter was painting, my ancestor was diligently scrutinizing his accounts, searching for some implication of fiduciary irresponsibility. The idea was to deny Velasquez his knighthood, of course, and my ancestor was not successful in this. He did succeed, however, by slowing things down for many years, just by industry and innuendo."

"Your family is very old," I said.

"Compared to yours, perhaps. Compared to this landscape, we are a few generations of mayflies. So why should I bother about them?"

"Because they are a very old family compared to mine," I said.

"A good point," he said, with the faintest of smiles on his lips, "perhaps I am rationalizing my obligation."

"You don't have to rationalize anything," I said flatly, "if you intend to pay me."

"So, perhaps I am slowing things down? Engaging in dilatory stratagems? Expressing my genetic proclivity? So, perhaps I am less free than I said I was."

"So, perhaps you should make an effort to get as free as you say you are," I said. Actually, I was in no hurry. I was tired of driving and had no intention of pressing matters toward their inevitable conclusion, since that would require my getting back behind the wheel. Still, the kid was getting on my nerves a little bit.

"Do you know the great tragedy of my family?" he said, continuing to slow things down. "The great tragedy is that we nearly had a pope. That is what my great aunts would tell me when I was a child. They would be dressing me for mass and they would say, 'Remember, we nearly had a pope. We would have had a pope,' they would say, 'were it not for that drunken sodomite from Avignon.'"

"Which drunken sodomite?" I asked.

"Oh…some French cardinal," he said, waving the fingers of one hand in front of his face as if he were brushing away a fly. "It's a family legend. The exact facts vary according to the person you are talking to. Either this arrogant frog refused to stay bribed and allowed the smoke to go up for an Italian. Or the noble cardinal died stinking drunk in the arms of a young priest on the night before the election. With the same consequences."

"Is that so bad?" I said. "Not having a pope?"

"Well, perhaps not. But having a pope is a very great honor. So, many of my great aunts date the decline of our family from that moment. From that moment we *nearly* had a pope."

"So you lost the Super Bowl," I said, "and the franchises went to hell."

He nearly laughed at this. "You are an extremely American person," he said.

"I am a gambler, Paco," I said. "I play the ponies. You don't have to tell me about bloodlines." I smiled when I said this because I was trying not to be angry with him. He was really not such a bad kid.

"Please, don't be angry with me," he said, picking up on it. "I bought this place so I could be alone. And now I am a little lonely in it."

"I understand," I said.

"You do?" he said.

"Yes. I understand that I have driven all the way out here to collect a loan that I made to a friend. And I understand that he is not going to pay me until he has told me everything that he wants to tell me. Everything he thinks I should know."

"So you do understand."

"That much, at least."

"Well, understand, too, that I have really stopped gambling. I look forward to visiting you, and not gambling the whole time I am there."

"You're always welcome," I said, "whether you gamble or not."

"I am ashamed that I lost so much, so foolishly, you know. But I am also a little ashamed that I can afford it."

"Now you sound like an American," I said. "But that's not what you wanted to tell me."

"No," he said. "I want to tell you about the greatest of my great uncles, the greatest of my ancestors. And about the greatest adventure in European history. The voyage of Columbus. That was a great adventure, was it not?"

"As adventures go," I said.

"And my ancestor was on that voyage, you see. But he was not an adventurer. He was a spy for the king. He was sent to spy on Columbus, of course, but most of all to spy on the queen's spies, who were spying on Columbus—and to make sure there was no breach of fiduciary responsibility in the expenditure of hemp, canvas and biscuit."

"A bean-counter," I said.

"A transatlantic bean-counting snitch on the greatest adventure in the history of Europeans," he said.

"That was his job," I said.

"Yes, and my ancestor did it well," he said. "He died in Hispaniola, of some American disease, I think. Or perhaps he was murdered. I don't know, but there was no disgrace in it, since he left exquisite records. Some of them were used later to prosecute Columbus."

"And that bothers you," I said.

"Well, how should I feel? I understand bean-counting, the need for it, and the need to slow things down, but when I was a child, I told my friends that my ancestor was a great adventurer, a dreamer. That he was with Columbus, not against him, trying to slow him down. Of course, if he had been with Columbus, he would have been in the vast minority on that voyage, since nearly everyone was against him, spying on him, or counting beans."

"So you wish somehow to redeem the guilt of your greatest ancestor. That is very American."

"No. I merely wished to transcend bean-counting, to speed things up, for once. So I sent my money forth to battle the baccarat shoe and hoped to follow it. But it sailed away into the slot and left me sitting there, where you found me."

"A lesson for us all," I said.

"A lesson for me, at least," he said, drawing a folded check from the pocket of his white linen shirt. Leaning forward, he handed it to me.

I unfolded the check. "This is for the full amount," I said. "Are you sure you can afford it?"

"All too sure," he said.

"I don't want to leave you short of walking-around money," I said.

"If I intended to walk around," he said, "I would not be short of money to do it with."

I slipped the check into my billfold and smiled at him. "You realize this leaves me with no reason to come back and visit you," I said. "If you only paid me half, I would have a reason to come back."

"Well, then I will come and visit you."

"And not gamble," I said, rising to my feet.

"And not gamble," he said. "From now on I will neither slow things down nor speed things up. I will ride the pulse of things and look at the desert."

"You have a nice place to do it from," I said. "Very nice."

I extended my hand to him. He rose to his feet and took it.

"Thank you, my friend," he said, clasping my hand in the two of his. "Of course, the floors are not yet what they should be, but I plan to work on them. Out here, where no one can see me working. Then, when the floors are correct, I will really be free."

A Walk to the Water

Patrick McCabe

In these corridors of white I see him still, padding away
on his wee soft feet. How long I've been here I do not
know. All I remember is the year 1975. I was living in a
flat in Brixton, London. That October a man walked
into a bar and was blown to bits. Through the smoke,
the sheeted dead trollied out one after the other. In
those days I lived on cream crackers and acid. The
opening bars of "Tubular Bells", they seemed to have
been going on forever. On the TV, a helicopter swung
out of Saigon and a refugee fell from a rope-ladder to
his death. I remember a guy with a face like a crocodile offering me a cup of tea. He shouldn't have had a
face like a crocodile. He shouldn't have because I knew
him. But I didn't know him now. I told him to leave me
alone or I'd do bad things. And I would have. His dripping jaws were terrible. That was why I screamed. They
brought me here soon after that.

They said not to worry. "It's going to take time,"
they whispered in my ear. "But it will be fine—you'll
see." I could see they were worried about me. They
didn't have to worry. I knew it would be fine. Sure
it would.

But little did I know just how fine until through the haze he came, on the softest of feet, just like in the days that used to be when he'd look at me and smile, my old friend Bunty. Wee Bunty from The Knacker's Yard, the happiest man in town. Four foot nothing, a tiny pillar of shining light. And those eyes of his still kind as ever.

"I'm not well, Bunty," I said. "I slipped away."

His eyelids went down slowly and he touched my arm with his warm and stubby fingers. Even though he couldn't speak, I knew what he was saying. He was saying: "It's all right, friend, your trouble's over. You're with Wee Bunty now. Wee Bunty will look after you forever!"

For the first time, for centuries it seemed, a silk parachute of calm enveloped me and I felt a tear come to my eye. At least I knew I was safe, his strong arms about me and his kind eyes giving me his soul. "I'm Wee Bunty," those eyes said. "I'm your friend and you are mine until the end of time."

For well I remembered him, far as could be from these corridors of white. "How are you, Bunty?" they'd cry. "How's the hammer hanging?" And Bunty Brady, would he smile. He'd smile forever.

Smile because he was the happiest man in town and had been for as far back as anyone could remember. Any time his name came up in conversation, you always knew you'd hear it said: "I met the bold Bunty coming across the square this morning, and do you know what I'm going to tell you—if there's a happier man alive in this town then I don't know about it!" To which the response would always be: "Now you're talking! Now you're fucking talking! Good man Bunty! It takes old Bunty every time!"

As indeed it did, coming walking down the street with a great big grin on his face, no matter what hour of the day or night you were likely to meet him. A grin that seemed to say: "I've just won the Irish Hospitals Sweepstakes," or "I've just inherited a fortune!" As the boys all said: "You have to admit it—he's a good one now! The happiest wee man ever trod shoe leather in this town!"

The great thing about Bunty was that his being "Yon height!" as The Horse McHenry called it, didn't seem to bother him at all. It no more bothered him than the man in the moon.

Which was impressive, it has to be said, for as far as everyone else was concerned, they knew only too well if they were saddled with not one, but two crosses the like of that—being no more than the height of a child and dumb from birth into the bargain—not only would there be no great big happy smiles or "Hello Missuses" or "That's not a bad day now, thank Gods!" but there'd be no seeing the light of day at all, for they'd be stuck inside the nearest pub drinking a bottle of whiskey a day if not more, looking at you with dead eyes that said only one thing: "Why me? Why does it have to be me? Why can't it be you? I'm like this and you don't care because it isn't you! You're glad I'm here praying for the day that four foot box goes in the ground! Don't lie to me! Don't lie to me, you fucking fucker! I know you are!"

And then blubber right up to the gills with tears. Of course that's what they would do. They knew only too well that that's how it would be. Wee men crying wee tears. Wee men with big bottles of whiskey. Boo hoo. Crying their baby eyes out.

But not Bunty Brady. O no—not Wee Bunty. He was a horse of a different colour. Which was why they never let an opportunity go by without praising him. There he'd be, smiling and laughing and joking away with all the kiddies who liked nothing better than to play half the day with the broken pump, the water spewing out of it like a great big giant umbrella. Sometimes it got all over Bunty and dribbled down his face and onto his clothes. If it had been anybody else, they'd have roared: "You stupid little bollockses! Look what you've gone and done to my good clothes! You've ruined my coat! You've ruined my trousers! What am I going to do now! Do you hear me! What am I going to do now!" But not him. No sir. As far as he was concerned, the water-chucking was just about the best yet! Laughing away and the kiddies dancing rings around him and water splashing down his cheeks into a great big puddle at his feet. Even the kids thought it was the wildest laughing they had ever heard—his wee old man's face scrunching up and the shoulders heaving away. "Jesus Mary and Joseph, man, but doesn't he cut a sketch," as the Horse said.

"Good man Bunty!" the boys'd say.

"Never a dull moment!" laughed The Horse. "Without our Bunty this bloody town'd bloody well keel over and die!"

Another thing about Bunty, of course, as they all knew well, was that he never seemed to sleep. O he had a bed all right, in a hayloft below The Knacker's Yard, but he was never there. What would he be there for? He was far too busy laughing and joking and being the funniest man out. Rarely a day went past then but I would meet him on the street or the square and say: "There you are, Bunty! That's not a bad day now!" and would be greeted with a grin so big you would have a job getting past it and that's a fact!

I'll never forget one day in particular, I was coming out of the church after saying a few prayers. It had to be just about the most beautiful day God in His wisdom had ever given to the earth. In the blue-sea sky not so much as a cloud stirred and behind me the organ pumped "Jesu Joy of Man's Desiring." Across the road, the breadman with a tray of loaves went whistling to the shop and the petrol pumps hummed merrily as a few rooks wildcat-tumbled on the slated roofs. "O day!" I said as I drank it in. "O day of all days that ever were!" Then who should I look up and see — only the man himself.

"There you are, Bunty!" says I. "Isn't that a day to lift your heart?"

And boy, did we laugh that day, and did we talk, this and that and the other, everything we talked about, from the tiniest incident to the most wonderful things that had ever happened in the town. "O, now you're talking!" Bunty would say with his eyes, his shoulders shaking and the hands rubbing and rasping to beat the band. Until at last the six bells of the Angelus tolled out across the sky and it was time for me to go.

"And so where are you off to, my old friend Bunty?" I said as I turned to go. "Off on your travels once more, I do expect!"

Well, such a grin as I got then, and would you believe it, to cap it all, a little stubby finger stuck in the air and, as an extra special bonus, a play the like of which you would not see on the television. Of course, I had seen plenty of old Bunty's plays before, him and his wee notes and his half-chewed pencil, but this, it has to be said, was by far the best play yet! The dancing and miming and antics of him, man. As The Horse might have said, it was a panic! It didn't take me long to work out where indeed he was bound on his travels. "So you're off to the lake, my old friend Bunty?" I said, and the wee head going like the clappers.

"And no better time to do it, my old friend," I said. "At six o'clock the water'll be just right. A swim is just the ticket!"

Or would have been if he hadn't gone all red in the face and started swatting the air, half-wild.

"So you're not off for a swim?" I said, and could see that that was right. And I was pleased to see the old smile return again as his eyes twinkled and I said: "So what takes you out there then?" Lord bless us, him and these bits of paper, writing away on them with his stubby pencil, the sweat gleaming on his forehead as he handed me one with the giant words: TO GET SOME PEACE printed on it. Well, whatever that was supposed to be about, tell you the truth it meant nothing to me at all, but good old Bunty he thought it was just great, his lips making the words TO GET SOME PEACE, TO GET SOME PEACE over and over, and the two of us laughing then, it got so bad I thought we'd never be able to stop! Bunty chewing away at the pencil and the shoulders going and if you had seen the pair of us you'd have been hard-pressed not to sign us up for Duffy's Circus. By the time we'd finished, I was just about sick from laughing and if you had said to me: "You're not to be allowed to laugh again ever in your life," it would have been just fine with me. By the time I left Bunty, my cheeks were flushed and there was a pain in my head, hammering away good-o. As I was crossing the square, the only thought that came into my mind was: "I think I could be doing without excitement the like of that for a while, thanks very much!" "Phew," was just about the only word I could manage to utter as I fell in the door of our house.

Not that I had any reason to be unduly worried about expecting that kind of excitement again in the near future or any other kind of future for that matter, as I found out the next day. The whole town was talking about it. The Horse was tearing up and down the street with the jacket flying, crying, "I saw him! I saw him just before he did it!" Of course, as they always do, a few liars claimed to have seen it coming "all along."

It was only "a matter of time," they said. The Horse chipped in and said: "I always knew there was something quare about him. Sure how would he be any other way, God love him. Do you know what I'm saying?"

The laugh of it was that when they found his clothes lying beneath a bush, they were so neatly folded and carefully arranged that you would think he had been getting ready to dickey himself up for an interview or something. God knows how many days they spent out at the lake, police sub-aqua teams and the whole lot. But it made no odds for in the end they never found him. After that, the lake became known as "The Bunty's Water," and any time you passed it from then on, all you could think of was good old Bunty and his big happy face.

You could sit there forever on the shining grass, with the sun high in the sky, the grasshoppers clacking and the birdies singing to their little baby fledglings, and every time you stared across the flat expanse of the still blue lake, you would think of him there, down there in its yawning maw, tumbling about like a wee astronaut adrift in the vastness of space, and then try not to hear when they came once more, the rotor blades, with their soft steady flutter, emerging from the aperture of light at the water's end, through which that old familiar cackle curved, and a smile flashed across the dripping jaws of a man with a crocodile face as his long fingers reached out for your throat, "Tubular Bells" chiming out peace over Saigon as he cooed: "Cream crackers and acid, perhaps? For my old friend who thought he'd never do bad things again? That's what you thought— is it, my friend? You thought it was over? Thought it was over, you stupid fuck? It's just beginning, you fool! It's just beginning!" warm blood pouring as with one deft wrist-flick your flesh it opened and spilt across the sky, the whupping blades drowning out the words: "Saigon to hell! On to pastures new, for more widows to weep, in the warm and pregnant belly of the Balkans!" your head bursting open like a pumpkin as the sky filled up

33

with light and from your own mouth rolled the screams of the sheeted dead trollied on squeaking wheels from the burning bar, a mocking spectral mute assembly, without end it seemed, when through the smoke you saw him floating towards you, light as a feather with his little limbs reaching, and you almost wept because now you knew it was going to be all right, just like they'd said it would, until he looked at you that way and at last, at last you heard the words upon his lips, those same two words that each day pulse inside your soul and inside these walls so infinite, so white:

Help me.
Help me.
Help me.

This Is Not It

Lynne Tillman

Whenever I arrive, it's the wrong time. No one has to tell me. The right time is a few minutes earlier or later. Invariably I arrive at the wrong time in the wrong place.

Wherever I am, it is the wrong place. It's not where I should be. No one says a word when I arrive. I am always unexpected.

Because it's the wrong place, I want to be someplace else. I always want to be in the place where I should have been. The place where I should have been is paradise on earth. It is inaccessible to me, because I cannot arrive on time at the right place.

(I try to be still.)

Because wherever I am is not where I should be, I am always ill at ease. I'm in an uncomfortable position. I have conversations with the wrong people. I should not be speaking to them. They know this, but everyone is polite since each of them may be similarly indisposed. They never remark that my presence is a problem to them. They put up with me; I put up with them. I always wonder when I can leave gracefully. I'm never graceful, because I don't fit in wherever I am.

(I try to control myself.)

In the wrong place at the wrong time, the wrong people and I are obviously in a drama, a tragedy or comedy. Whatever tragedy I am in, unwittingly and involuntarily, it's not the right one for me. It's either too grand or pathetic, an exaggeration, considering my position or station, which is an impossible one. A neighbouring tragedy, the one next door, would be better for me. But it is unavailable to me. It is doubtless the tragedy I was born to. But my tragedy would not be invigorated by comparison. Just the opposite. The emptiness at its center, with me as the wrong hero, makes it funny. People laugh at my dilemma. In someone else's tragedy, my dilemma would be acknowledged appropriately.

(I try to be unobtrusive.)

Whatever comedy I am in, whenever I inadvertently participate, it is being played by overly tragic people. It's the wrong comedy. I am unsuitably sad. I forget the punchlines and tell jokes badly, with the wrong timing. People cry at my ill-timed jokes. I cry when I should laugh. When I am mistakenly in the audience, at someone else's tragedy or comedy, my reactions are consistently wrong.

(I try to leave.)

Whenever I attempt to go, I ask a friend which is the right way. But whoever is my friend is the wrong friend.

This is not the person who should be my friend. Even if this person is a friend, he or she may provide the wrong advice. Or this friend may tell me to find the information I need in a book.

(I try to be sensible.)

Whatever book I find is the wrong book. The right book is on the shelf, in the bookstore or library, next to the wrong one I discover. Once I have it and begin to read it, I know it's the wrong book. No wrong book will tell me what I need to know, but I keep buying and reading books. I buy the same books again and again. Because I put them away in the wrong place, I forget I already have them.

(I try to find myself.)

Whenever I flee to a place I think I've never been, I discover that I've been there before. I hated the place on my first visit, but I've repressed the memory of it. I return to the hated places often. I have seen many movies again, too. I go twice to places and to see people and movies I should never have visited or seen in the first place.

(I try to abstain.)

Whenever I see myself in a mirror, I don't believe the person is me. I believe I'm seeing the wrong person. This person masquerades as me. I try to catch this person unaware by sneaking up to surprise the mirror image. I am always disappointed when the wrong person shows up. The wrong person consistently makes the wrong appearance.

(I try not to trust appearances.)

Since I am in the wrong place, it must be the wrong mirror. The wrong mirror must not mirror the right image. It can't be me. But I keep looking. I may simply be the wrong person.

(I try not to want to escape. I try not to cry or laugh. I try to remember. I try to act differently.)

If I am the wrong person, this must be why, whatever world I am in, there is a better one elsewhere. Whatever money I have, more money is waiting somewhere else. This is why I do not like what I see. It is why I don't want what I have and why I want what is nearby.

Whatever I have is not what I should have. Whatever makes me happy ultimately makes me sad. I am the wrong person living my life. Someone somewhere else must be better off.

(I try to fool myself.)

Whoever I am, I am wrong. I try not to expect anything. It's impossible not to expect the wrong things in life. But I can't expect nothing. Nothing's certain. This may be wrong.

(I try not to jump to conclusions.)

Unhinged

Adrian Searle

I. Complaint

Dear Sir,

I wish to further my complaint about the goings-on in the property we rent from you. I must once again refer you to our numerous prior exchanges on this matter over the past 18 months. Your previous responses have been both tardy and evasive, even though you told me, September last, when I finally managed to track you down in person, that the matter was "in hand". It is now, I might remind you, February.

I will no longer be fobbed-off with your promises and delays. My wife has become quite unwell because of the continued disturbances, and after the events which occurred yesterday, now says that she refuses to spend another night on the premises. She is, as you know, already under the doctor because of it. I do not understand why you refuse to take us seriously, and why the activities of the occupant of the flat above our own should be allowed to go on uninvestigated. You are, after all, the agent to whom we pay our rents, both for tenure and for services, although we have seen precious little of the latter, but I shan't take you up on that here.

This last week we have been forced to take our complaint to the police, but as the events occur on private property they refuse to do anything, and tell us that this is merely a "domestic" dispute. A junior officer even went so far as to suggest that we were troublemakers. I now feel we have no choice but to petition you to put a stop to it. You have previously suggested that we may be experiencing what you called "an acoustic effect" caused by our proximity to a main road and the disposition of walls, etcetera, in the vicinity. We are neither troublemakers nor are we of the imaginative sort. Furthermore, I can assure you that we are not the kind of people who suffer from effects of any kind, let alone acoustic ones.

The events of last night were certainly not imaginary, and nor was it the sound of the traffic outside. It is also not feasible that the noises emanating through our ceiling from the floor above could be the television, the radio or a record player. Nor could it be possible that the person upstairs keeps horses in his room. A concert party has also been—to my mind, implausibly—offered as a cause, but we would have been certain to hear the guests arriving by the stairs. There were none. I find your suggestion that it is "merely the noise of the occupant walking about on his carpet and clearing his throat," or "engaging in a few necessary nocturnal repairs," laughable and derisory. Pray do not use your patronising tone with me again, as I can see right through it and find it most unhelpful.

Why you refuse to come here yourself, just because these disturbances occur after business hours, is beyond me. You say that you are merely the agent, and that it is a matter to take up with the owner, but the letters we have sent to him are returned unopened. I am coming to the conclusion that you either do not take us seriously or that you are, in some way, colluding in the matter—but I suppose I must banish that thought from my mind and presume instead that affairs of business have somehow prevented you from paying full attention to our cause. The final suggestion you made to us in your last missive, i.e. that our neighbour may be conducting seances of some sort, quite goes against the terms of the lease, as you well know. If it is seances going on up there they ought to be prevented, forthwith.

I do not know how properly to describe the noise and the vibration. The whole building seems to shudder. At about 11 o'clock last night, just after we had retired, it began again, with the sound of feet. A great many feet, going this way and that, right across our ceiling; I did my military service, and I know the sound of feet when I hear them. And it isn't just ordinary feet, it isn't the sound of a man walking about in his carpet slippers; this was feet with boots on, and women as well. You can tell when they are wearing those high heels. The noise of water is also very worrying—you think the ceiling might go at any minute. And even if he has taken up his carpets and is stamping about on the floorboards or moving his furniture, it wouldn't sound anything like the cacophony I'm describing. And with the water there would be the problem of wetness, of seepage and damp, which thankfully we have not as yet suffered, although I'm sure it is only a matter of time, however adequately our ceiling is plastered and no matter how resilient his carpeting. We can discount carpets in any case: these are the sounds of people walking about on the pavement, on cobbles. You can hear walking sticks or canes distinctly. There is a great deal of tapping. I did wonder whether it might be a snooker table or billiards he'd got up there but the stairs aren't wide enough, not even for a small one.

Worst of all is the rumbling, a rumbling accompanied by horse's hooves. It goes right from one wall to the other, sometimes in both directions at once. And you can hear raised voices and shouting but you can't make out the words. Mostly men but quite often women and sometimes children as well. Children and babies crying, which always makes my wife upset because she could never have any. I'd get more peace if I went and lay down in the middle of the road, which is precisely the kind of hullabaloo I'm talking about.

At half past four last night, all went quiet for a while and then at about ten-to the hour I heard this pattering, not like feet this time, but like hundreds of dripping taps or even rain. I got up and looked out the window and it was a perfectly clear night, though still dark. It was definitely the sound of rain, not a shower or drizzle but an absolute downpour and extremely loud, a very great deal of rain. Once or twice there were feet again, hurrying, but mostly just the noise of the rain, and as it went on you could actually hear sloshing, as though the whole of upstairs were being flooded, although our ceiling remained as ever, quite unaffected. I'm sure I heard a bicycle bell at one point, but far-off, and then someone swearing, right in my ear, before I finally managed to drift off, although my wife says she got no rest at all, and hasn't in weeks.

Some nights there is only muttering and at other times the sound of doors banging. But when I go up there and put my ear to his door it is like the tomb, not even a clock ticking. Perhaps it's insulated. And when I knock and call out as loud as I can, even though I know he's in there, I have never once had a reply.

I have waited for our neighbour all day on the stairs, and have never seen him. I did hear his door close and the lock turn, and leapt out hoping to catch him on his way in or out, but have never once managed to gain a glimpse of him. Always I am faced with a closed door. It is an insult, to be kept standing there in front of a closed door with no answer forthcoming however hard I knock. This has happened innumerable times. He does not respond to notes pushed under his door, or to letters sent via the usual channels, nor even telegrams.

I have not succeeded in gaining his telephone number, despite enquiries, and I do not know if he even has one. Moreover, I have never once set foot in his lodgings. That is the only way to get to the bottom of it, to get in there and sort him out. I do not know him, and would not recognise him if we passed on the street or stood in the same queue in the baker's or chemist. I have even enquired of other local residents and trades people if they can point him out to me, but all to no avail. I fear I am becoming something of a laughing stock. As far as I can ascertain, he receives neither letters nor visitors. The worst is, I feel certain he knows me, and my wife as well, who is entirely blameless. I am getting the distinct impression that our neighbour is by some foul and devious means trying to remove us from this house and that you are in it with him. My wife and I are quite unhinged by our nightly disturbances, and can take it no longer. What we insist upon is explanation and remedy and compensation—nothing else will do.

Yours faithfully, etc.

II. Rooms

In one room, a broken telephone. In another, an empty wardrobe and a raincoat hung from a hook on the back of the door. The plaster bust of a Turk wearing a fez sits on a table in the study. The floor is strewn with books. At the far end of this room, beyond the armchair and the half-open shutters, one can just perceive the silhouette of a man leaning over the balcony. He has not moved for a long time.

Outside, at one end of the street, is a small square, in the centre of which stands a statue of the local philanthropist and benefactor, after whom the street was named in the earlier part of the previous century. Most passers-by assume him to be some military man, or a politician, and few stop to read the name carved in the plinth. On the far side of the square a church rises above the plane trees. The thoroughfare itself is lined with common shops, among them a shoe mender's, a bakery, a haberdasher's, a barber, a second-hand book shop and dealer in prints, a pharmacy, and a drapery. At the other end of the street stands a market.

It is possible, leaning on any one of the many balconies on the second and third floors, to survey the street from one end to the other. One can watch the couples sitting and strolling round the square, the group of children playing in the shadow of the statue, the solitaries with time on their hands, the bustle of shoppers and delivery wagons around the market. Private offices and small workshops now occupy the first floors of some of the buildings: a solicitor above the pharmacy, a picture-framer and restorer at number 12, over the bookseller's, a shipping office at number 18. It is an ordinary street, such as might be found anywhere.

On this street live 35 married couples, 8 widows, 5 widowers, 87 unmarried persons of all ages, 2 felons who have completed their term and one yet to begin his. Before he does, he must first commit his crime, he must be caught, there must be a trial, and then he will achieve a brief notoriety. For two memorable days and nights the little square at the end of the street will be cordoned off and there will be much to-ing and fro-ing of officialdom: the police, officers of the town council, the medical authorities, and a huddle of reporters.

Forty seven children under the age of 14 live in this street at the time of writing, though 3 will die in an outbreak of meningitis before the year is out and one will very soon be knocked down and killed by a passing van.

An amateur music hall artiste lives at number 18. He shares his life with a ventriloquist's dummy and a doting wife. He sees the child step out from the kerb, attempts to call out, and takes a step towards her, but now she is lying dead in the gutter with her neck broken. A crowd has gathered, but the van has gone. Later that afternoon his wife, returning home, will find her husband crouched on their bed, cradling the dummy in his arms.

At number 2, there is a young man who is seriously thinking about suicide (though by next week a piece of good fortune will rescue him, and in later years he will remember how petty his worries at the time really were). There are several alcoholics and one drug addict living in the street. The addict is of the old-fashioned sort, who entered upon a course of morphine during his treatment for a tumor, but while the cancer retreated, his addiction grew, and he has subsequently been unable to wean himself from the opiate. He plays chess with the pharmacist, and invariably wins. A man at number 17 is some kind of writer. The African at number 14 is studying theology and will one day become Minister of Education in the first post-colonial government of his country. There will be no statue of him after the subsequent coup.

Two old sisters at number 9 listen to the prostitute whose rooms abut their own. They press their ears to the partition wall, listening for the faint groans and sighs and the rhythmic creaking of a bed. This has become their daily entertainment, although they never speak of it—in fact, they never converse at all, and communicate instead by leaving notes to one another. These are to be found on the mantelpiece, the kitchen table, on the little bamboo stand in the hall, even in the bathroom and the pantry. The notes have accumulated over the years on every available surface, and it is impossible for either one of the sisters to tell, except by the signs of fading, foxing stains and decrepitude, whether any one of these little missives is of recent origin or belongs to some forgotten period in the past. It does not matter a great deal, as the daily round of their lives has become unalterable, and has been so for as long as either can remember. The notes themselves, always dealing with similar subjects—shopping arrangements, the state of the plumbing or one another's bowels, the clemency or otherwise of the season (and who last had the umbrella, and where did they leave it?), the constant re-apportioning of the various legacies they intend to leave in their respective wills (an interminable subject of controversy), the dividing of bills, the whereabouts of one or the other's reading glasses (forever being mislaid), and so on—are themselves both of permanent relevance and at the same time utterly misleading and out of date. As the two old ladies' handwriting is, to their myopic eyes, indistinguishable, neither can tell whether they are responding to a note they have received from the other or to a note they wrote themselves. In their small apartment, time runs in several directions at once.

Friedmann lives at number 23, on the third floor.

III. Unhinged

Friedmann had begun to wonder whether he was being spied upon. But the signs were so subtle that he was never certain it was not he himself who had misplaced a paper, or set down a book from the shelf—a book he thought he hadn't touched in years. He'd lived alone too long, had so few contacts with the world beyond his walls, that he no longer trusted his own judgment. Yesterday morning, for example, he wondered whether he was being followed, and in the baker's shop a mousy little man in the queue had given him a defiant and hostile stare. Perhaps, it struck him now, people found him odd. The thought saddened him and compounded his unease.

But today, Friedmann had returned to his room to find everything in its place, just as it should be, just as he had left it. The flowers had continued to wilt at their usual rate, lightly dropping petals on the table. He stood on his balcony, trying to compose himself. He stood on his balcony for a long time; he did not move.

Such days as these. I watch them all, swirling beneath my feet; the two old ladies, dressed nearly alike, they must be sisters, yet even though they walk together they never take one another's arm nor share a word. The same time every day, a loaf, a turn around the park, feed the pigeons. There they go. There's something about a routine, comforting at that age.

Through the wall he heard raised voices.

Why can't they stop that damned row. Always the same thing, you'd think they'd invent something new to shout about. But it's always the same thing, doesn't matter who you're with, it always comes down to fucking and money. This time they're pretending it's the stairs—"You should write to the agent, get onto him." If only it was the bloody stairs, they'd sort it out. I'd get onto him myself if it would make a blind bit of difference, except I am the sodding agent, tenant, and owner rolled into one. Why didn't he sell it, I begged him but he never did, just filled it with his crap, his books and papers and rented it out so he could fuck off wherever and whenever no thought for me after Mother went. Hit the Andes like a wall, no sign of a will and I can't sell it. A helicopter, at his age. Should've jumped off the balcony at his age, gone in his sleep or a nice heart attack on a park bench, handy for the church. My dear Father.

He remembered his parents arguing. He remembered their quarrels, and a door slamming, shutting him out. He had lain there on his stomach, the fierce odour of the hall carpet in his nostrils, watching their feet pass this way and that under the door, blurred shadows moving in the sharp strip of light. This was his first movie. As much as this scene frightened and confused him he also took a particular pleasure in it, as the exclusive audience. Mesmerised, he traced the fault-lines in his parents' world, without realising that the same cracks ran right through his own.

Early in the afternoon, lost in thought on his balcony, Friedmann was disturbed by a commotion further down the street, a shout from below, a horn, some kind of accident which immediately drew a crowd and set people running in several directions.

Jesus, the kid. She was under the balcony a second ago, then when that guy came out of the alley carrying the ladder I saw her, just now, chasing the other kid, the one I thought was late, I saw her. Jumped into the gutter to go round straight under the wheels. Fucking Christ she's all at the wrong angle, her head shouldn't be like that. Where's he going? Can't just drive off, what about the kid?

Now he's at it again downstairs. I'd like him to be up here now, I'd show him something to complain about. I suppose he'd only get onto the town hall about the traffic laws, with her lying dead at his feet. "Dear Sir, I am writing this in plain view of the corpse of an under-age person bleeding on the pavement below me. I feel sure that this is contrary to the Obstruction of the Highway bylaws and am taking this opportunity to remind the council of its duties." He'll be up here soon enough, you wait.

He turned and went back inside, uninterested. He settled into his armchair and picked up a book from the pile at his feet. Blunt on Borromini, one of the books from his father's collection. Annoyed, he slammed it shut and smelt the rising dust. The books must go, he thought, down to the second-hand place.

It grew dark. Closing the shutters, his reflection peered back at him through the slats.

A dry cough from the other side of Friedmann's door, less the sound of someone clearing his throat than someone trying to attract attention. Friedmann on one side of the door, his unseen visitor on the other.

"You'll oblige me, Sir, with a word."

Friedmann said nothing, did not move.

"I know you're in there."

Friedmann made no reply.

"You've got to come out sometime. I'll wait all night if needs be."

But the voice more peevish this time, more of a whine, more like an overtired and fractious child. Friedmann opened his mouth, about to speak, yet no words came. He didn't begin to breathe again until the man had gone away.

IV. Rain Room

It is raining. The street is empty. Up and down the street, lights go on and off, doors open and close. Even the whore has finished her business till tomorrow. She turns uncomfortably in bed. In a back room at number 19 there's an insomniac cheating at solitaire. The baker has been up an hour already, and has just taken the first batch of loaves from his oven. The writer sits at his table, worrying over the sentence he has just written. It reads, "It is raining, the street is empty." He wonders whether to exchange the comma for a full stop, to make two sentences. He also wonders whether he wrote this absently, because the fact that it is raining and that the street is empty have just impinged themselves on his consciousness. For the past three hours his thoughts have been consumed entirely by the fate of his characters, and he has lost the thread. He is struck, suddenly, by how tired he is, and goes to the mirror to wash his face. The barber at number 26 is down to his last whiskey. At number 15 an unfaithful wife has cried herself to sleep, for today she was found out. Her husband, the bookseller, sleeps on the sofa. Tomorrow she will take their children to her mother's in the country, where she will lie about the reason for her visit.

Friedmann, surfacing from deep water, switches on the bedside lamp. The glare of his room, the walls too hot to touch; the burning flowers, the groaning books, the clock churning through the hours. He rises and dresses, hurriedly. Hear him rummaging about, banging into things, opening and closing cupboards, a man oblivious, at large in the dormitories of the night.

The father of the child who died today stares at the wallpaper, unseeing. A mother grieving. The miscreant who is about to commit his crime is fast asleep. A baby wakes.

The first traffic passes on the street below, loaded with produce for market, their wheels scraping and rumbling over the wet cobbles. Their noise and Friedmann's groans cannot be told apart, as he dreams he lies abed, dreaming he dreams a dreamless sleep, waking to a normal day. Instead he is on the street, hurrying for the statue and the shelter of trees. He curses as he plunges through the water in the gutter. A woman passes him by, urging her children forward at a pace. Come along, stop dragging your feet, she says. It's no one. Her youngest child, perched on his brother's shoulders, turns to face him with a grin. A cyclist, off early to work, rings his bell as he rounds the corner. Someone steps in a puddle and swears loudly.

All this takes place on the third floor of number 23. On the floor below a sleepless couple, rigid in the twisted sheets, their eyes fixed on the ceiling, await the morning.

V. Banisters

Dear Sir,

As you have not given me the courtesy of a reply, I must refer you to my letter of last February.

Since my last communication with you the house has been mysteriously quiet—although I am sure you are aware, as it has been in all the papers, of the terrible goings-on elsewhere in our little street, and the park was closed off for days. But of our neighbor their has been no sign and—thankfully—a complete remission of the disturbances. We have, however, had men here going through his rooms and asking all kinds of questions whose relevance I fail to comprehend. They have left an awful lot of mud on the stairs and, in the removal of the upstairs occupant's belongings, have damaged and scuffed both the wallpaper and the banisters no end. We shall certainly need a new hand-rail, or perhaps it could be sandeddown. There could be an accident, especially given my wife's nerves.

As to the cause of our erstwhile neighbour's flight, I can give no explanation. They've even had the floorboards up, as far as I can tell. Where our Mr. Friedmann (we have all, at last, learned his name) has gone off to I've no idea, though there was some talk, which I heard from an acquaintance, who got it from our chemist (though why he should know I've no idea), that he had returned to South America, where apparently his father worked, years ago. Perhaps our neighbourhood can soon return to its former self, and our house to a tranquil state.

I understand that new tenants have been found for upstairs, a pair of elderly sisters who previously lived at number 9, forced out of their lodgings by the activities of a young woman of dubious reputation who had a constant stream of gentlemen callers at all hours. I can assure you that they'll be troubled by no such unsavory characters here.

Meanwhile, I must insist that the necessary repairs which I assume come under your "service charge" will be carried out forthwith. Until the banisters have been sorted out, I am afraid that I intend to withhold any monies owing on that account.

I remain yours, Sir, Yours, etc.

The Ventriloquist's Opera

William Forsythe

The other day I encountered a dummy who said that it knew the libretto of L'ARUT CE TIHCRA, a ventriloquist's opera. I expressed curiosity and asked the dummy to recount the story if it possibly could.

As the dummy began I realized that its voice was not its own and I'm still puzzled as to the location of the voice which animated its speech. What follows is the libretto.

Act I

Tableau: A vivid evocation of what is left to be done.

Scene 1: A small crowd gathers elsewhere. In unison, they consider their ultimate withdrawal (the tenors are already off-stage).

Chorus: Back through the mirror, etc. (Nomads wander off up left). The scene is bereft of illumination; Java, represented on minute scraps of paper, is falling towards the floor of the stage, lending the scene the appropriate realism it had been intentionally lacking.

Supertitle up in 15 sec on proscenium:
BLASPHEMY, PARODY, SANITY, PHRASE

Aria-Soprano: Your time will be wasted at the same rate by everyone whose time will be wasted by everyone at the same rate as everyone else wastes your time; vague tonal references to the closing theme.

A screen descends.

NOTHING DOESN'T APPEAR is projected until bar 733, at which point the stage manager (a character) portrayed as a member of the chorus issues a warning to members of what appear to be a kind of "jury" (covered with the aforementioned papery precipitate) located center stage.
Their sudden appearances have been accomplished through an arrangement of trap doors concealed in the immense snow-covered projection equipment (deployed during the aforementioned projection scene) which is situated on stage so as to conceal this entrance of the "pseudo" jury, who are now clearly to be identified as experts of some sort.

The snow: A complex system of blowers and exhaust fans ingeniously allow a text to form in the air using only the falling paper particles.

Ever-more elaborate descriptions of proliferation and perfect disorder seem to transform their own moving layers of construction into geometrical superimpositions of the words IT'S NOW! Just as the swirling texts become precise the scene comes suddenly to a halt.

Astoundingly, the elaborate projection equipment disappears at precisely the same instant, revealing it also to be the result of the illusion created by the ingenious system of blowers (hence its snow-covered appearance). As the text vanishes (as indicated) so does the jury of experts!

Recitativo: (cast as yet undecided) the screen now provides silent accompaniment for the singer by displaying the notation of the tacit orchestral accompaniment.

At this point, a rhetorical dramatic device allows the soloist to report that the disappearance of the immense technical equipment which had supposedly permitted the ingenious appearance of the snow-covered experts was simply a device to expose the fact that the snow was not snow at all but minute shreds of the missing score which accompanied that particular scene. Alas, the scene ends as vividly as it began.

Scene II The Ballet

A large map of Java is being traced in the now-drifted remains of the score. Figures attired for their own protection shuffle about the scene, lending ever-more precise geographical detail to the representation. Great attention is given to recreating the subtle curvature of the earth. The obsessive attempts of the performers are nonetheless thwarted by the very site of their endeavors, namely: THE STAGE!

It seems that cracks in the surface supporting the performers and their "map" are allowing innumerable pieces of the mapped score to slip through and fall into the adjoining space on the other side! At this point a peculiar stroke of fate comes into play.

A camera normally deployed as a security device in the sub-stage captures the fall of the fragments in a series of freeze-frames which arouse the attention of the security person in charge! It seems that the camera has captured successive moments of configuration that produce a sequence of words that inform the person in charge of an impending disaster in that very theater!

The person in charge of security (perhaps a little too hastily) decides that the danger is immanently electrical and cuts the power to the theater, plunging the theater into theatrical darkness. (A recording of the ensuing noises typical of contemporary theatrical panic).

As ingenious as the projection of light is the projection of sound, and as the audience is prepared to be susceptible to effect, it cannot voluntarily perceive the resulting mêlée as simulated, at least not in the dark. In the ensuing rush for the exits both performers and audience fall through the aforementioned cracks in the performing surface and thereby obliterate the theatrical Java with its subtle global curve.

Those performers and members of the audience who fall through the cracks are miraculously (hymn from chorus—off) saved/suspended by the intricate geometries of the under-stage machinery.

All are confused, exhilarated, furious.

Help arrives (costumes to be decided...)

After careful investigation, the rescue party concedes that all those on the other side of what was once Java are so inextricably entangled in the lattice-work of dangerous machinery that only a radical attempt at rescue will save anything at all.

It seems the mechanism that supports and threatens both viewers and performers must be reprogrammed to dislodge the very stage it supports. The sophistication and complexity of the systems that operate the ensnaring/lifesaving theatrical mechanism prove daunting to the well-intended unensnared.

(please note, this is still the Ballet)

Nonetheless, the moment for rescue has arrived and the switch is thrown.

The machinery engages as follows:

Imagine the surface of a stage being lifted from its foundations and suspended in a manner that allows it to rotate omnidirectionally from any point or line on its structure. This mobility allows the surface to slide along its own edges, rotating and extending from any point on the surface or edge of the plane.

The ensuing configurations rotate and slide along the previous angular displacements in a similar manner, producing a blur of juxtaposition. By sheer accident (for no one knows what will really happen), all previous mechanisms and machineries hitherto deployed in the production engage. The result being a multitude of suspended precipitate texts in the slicing vortex of the previously mentioned planar spinnings. Naturally, the performers and audience are thrown about the room, passing through, or rather, permeating the stage surface in an osmotic manner.

The entire mechanism at once collapses into a field of minute shreds not unlike those used for the global effect in the previous scene. The results bear slight resemblance to territory yet uncharted, ostensibly through, or due to, some oversight. A single artifact remains:

The flickering monitor of the security camera, which has registered the last moment of the rescue.

The image resembles a ghostly dance on the underside of Java.

END OF ACT

CURTAIN

At this point the dummy stops his narrative and confesses that he was talking to himself (impossible), and falls silent, through one of the cracks in the stage.

The Belled Girl Sends a Tape to an Impresario

Marina Warner

Dear Mr. Orlowski, I hope you will listen to me on this tape I am sending it to you, Dr. Mandell says he knows how to get it to you, he nodded when I said you would understand me because I understood everything you said, every single thing you said speaks straight to me; you and me are brother and sister, flesh and blood, or perhaps born at the same hour on the same day, you in Kansas City (I think you said you were born in Kansas City) and me in Bristol. Star twins, that's what we are. From what you said, I know we have identical souls and that you could take me away from here like you took those boys you were talking about away from the place they were sectioned, no, perhaps not sectioned, but kept. I am kept here, too, and I could do things for you like they did. I can speak, you're hearing my voice on this tape, I hope it sounds nice—I'm talking to you now, I have a nice voice, everyone tells me so, it has a tinkling sound, like spring water, like fairyland! But I'm running ahead of myself, I must take things one at a time and try and not let things get jumbled up... More haste, less speed, that's what the nurses like to say. You said that one of the boys you took away from the place where he was kept couldn't even talk at all when you started. You made noises and suddenly you screwed your face up, your mouth and eyes all twisted to show us how difficult it was for him to make words. Your face looked so different when you were showing us his handicap (handicapped—that's the word for it, that's something else I'm going to come to, in a moment). At one moment you were calm and beautiful, your face smiling and smooth like the angel with the candle in the chapel here where I go sometimes to ask that someone like you comes and lets me out of here. You drew with your finger in the air a cube and you said it was made of glass and sparkled and that your theatre was like that, an imaginary place where everything was clear and pure and safe and beautiful and then you showed us a photograph of him, of the Gentle Giant in your play. Casey, his name is, you said, and you could hear what he was saying through all those funny noises, that heehawing and spluttering—Amy who often sits beside me in the day room does that too, sometimes, when we're meant to be having quiet time. But you could understand what was lovely and wise and deep underneath and in the heart of him, trapped inside that horrible mumbling and stuttering Casey was doing. And he was only twelve years old then, eight years ago, you said, when you first took him in. The audience loved it when you told how you had asked the judge if you could adopt him and the judge had said, no, he'd have to go to a home but you said it would cost the state so much more money to do that than to let him go home with you instead. It was easy to see you loved him. Well, I know you could understand me even more because I...you see, I can talk to you. And I can perform—you wouldn't even need to teach me to dance and play, I can do lots of numbers, I've had lessons. I can twirl and ring the whole of The Beatles's first album: "She Loves You, Yeah Yeah," "Love, Love Me Do," "Money, That's What I Want," and "I Wanna Hold Her Hand"—that's funny, really. But my audiences like it. I'm used to tumultuous applause. I'd spin round and round and take my curtain call dizzy from the public's love. Casey you said was a star, you made him the star of your show, there was a photograph of him, sultry eyes, big slick quiff of hair and snaketight jeans on a throne with a long drape flowing down the stage from beneath his feet and the light falling on him like a halo. Well, I would do anything for you if you did all that for me. Because I loved you when I first saw you last night on the telly. And you haven't tried the same with a girl, not yet, have you? Well, I am the one, Lynton, Mr. Orlowski. I'll be much better than Casey who couldn't speak, not properly at least. You can hear how well I talk, I swear this is all just coming out, without anyone helping me, no doctors around, I'm on my own, just you and me and the machine. I can also scat a bit when I sing too, I am fearless when I am in front of my public. I will be perfect I will perform I won't flag I'll dance and sing: Here, Listen! Just a verse so you know what I can do:

She loves you, yeah yeah...
Hear the bells?

This is why: I'll tell you the story, it's simple really but lots of people don't believe me when I tell it. That's why I'm sending you this, because you will. Like you could see through Casey's noises, you'll see me. And then you'll know I'm made for you to take away with you. That it wouldn't be like two people together, but just one person. Two bodies, yes, but joined in one soul.

I was living in Bristol, I think I mentioned that, in a small house with a garden front and back, no weeds in the tiled path to the front porch, my mother always hung the washing low so that neighbours wouldn't get a peek at our underwear, so she said. The school bus stopped just down the road, and I had time to run out when I heard the driver turn the corner, changing gear and throbbing. I'd plaits then, which Mum used to do for me, with ribbons tied over elastic bands, otherwise they'd fall off because my hair is really silky. And when she did her nails, she'd let me do mine, too, dab it on for me, I liked the smell when I waved my fingertips about to dry them, like Mum did. Frosted Rose was her best colour, I think, but Cinnamon Gold was good, too.

Sometimes I'd do different nails different colours, you know, to try them out.

On Thursdays, I wouldn't come back with the others on the bus, but go to my ballet lessons. Miss Morris, she used to tap our feet with a little wand to make us stick them out at the widest angle and hollow our backs and pull in our bottoms. Tuck that tail in! she'd bellow. I had very expressive hands, she would say to the class, and point at them with her wand, and sometimes lift my arm a little with it to adjust the pose in the mirror. Sometimes she put one of my hands—they were small and quite pudgy then—in her palm and then she'd stroke it smooth, like it was covered in velvet with the pile running one way, and then she'd bend the fingers down and lift my arm and check in the mirror and tell the whole class to look at my port de bras and stop being such hephalumps and take a cue from Phoebe Jones. You can see I was her favorite.

Miss Morris had small feet and the elastic of her ballet slippers made her instep into two plump mounds like the halves of a peach—she wore thick pinky-brown tights too. She was a character dancer when she was young; she once danced a mad nun at the Royal Opera House. Her brother—you probably know him—is the actor who plays Kevin in Streetwise at 5.15 on Thursdays with a repeat on Monday I always miss because it's my time in the hot baths here. Miss Morris smelled of fags and talcum powder all mixed up. One day she came home to see Mum and Dad and told them I had a future and should go to a proper dance academy. So that's how I came to go to London when I was still titchy.

My hands were my "passport to success." More than my legs, Miss Morris knew. She advised me to build on my strengths. "They're your capital, darling," she'd say. This was when things got weird. You see, whatever people were saying about them I couldn't believe. Friends in class would hold theirs up next to mine and the nice ones would groan and cry "It's not fair!" and the not so nice ones would look squintily and tighten their lips and I could feel their hate slam down on my hands like a hammer. I won't repeat what was said— you'd think I was boasting. My boyfriend then was Lucas Tring, one of the Tring family, you know them, too, that meant something to me, music hall, circus, dance, show biz, for generations, and he wouldn't let me do anything, kept looking up insurance brochures to see what was the best deal he could buy to "cover any loss". He stopped me even washing up my tights in the basin saying he'd do all that for me so that my hands wouldn't spoil. He and I were renting together off the Earl's Court Road and that's when things began to go really weird. No, I suppose they had been for a while, as I said, except that I hadn't noticed. He was an artist, he kept on saying, and I was his muse. He was planning a show, he wanted to be someone like you, Mr. Orlowski—I hope you're still there—he was designing the lights and the choreography, it was a puppet version of The Little Mermaid, with my hands in whiteface dancing the parts in a black box like a Punch and Judy booth. But I kept not doing the movements right. I kept falling over myself. I was all fingers and thumbs! And he was shouting at me. Then he'd grab my hands and massage them with oils and breathe on them…and he wouldn't let me use them even to…you know, when we were in bed. He'd wrap them in silken bags with ribbons at the wrists.

I knew my hands were deteriorating every day, minute by minute, that if Miss Morris saw them now she'd notice they were getting wrinkled like an autumn leaf and the pores showing like someone had pricked out a paper pattern in the skin. The joints thickening and the tips flattening and the colour changing under the make-up, so that liver spots were just round the corner. I was beginning to find it hard to show them at all. I began pretending I had cramps so that I could get out of appearing, not have to perform any more. I stopped functioning, really. Then one morning I woke up and I couldn't move. I could not lift a finger, literally.

While I was lying in bed, though it felt as if I was lying kind of above the bed, suspended like the girl who gets sawn in half at the circus, a doctor came to see me and he gave me the idea for the cure. He said I should have a transplant, it would be simple. Plenty of people would be glad of a pair of hands like mine, they'd be very useful to someone, even if they didn't do me any good any longer. He had a big black hat with a wide brim and silver buckles on old-fashioned shoes and black stockings and he spoke in a soft voice—he was an American, like you! I helped him draw a circle round me with white chalk in my space above the bed and then I closed my eyes. There was no blood. He put my hands in a shoe box, wrapped in the neckerchief he had been wearing, and they did look beautiful, the knuckles dimpled just so, the backs smooth as ivory and each finger gracefully angled in relation to its neighbour. I was proud to be giving them away to someone who would know how to use them.

My bells play very prettily. You know bells are very unusual instruments, lively, with lots of character. My left bell rings in C and the other in F sharp which makes a lovely, solid chord, rings of sounds that go out and out for miles around me, humming high and low and just a little bit dissonant, which gives an edge to my tinkling, I can tell you! I play almost any song-and-dance routine you care to name, and I'd be pleased to—especially for you. So I'm still a wonder of the world—a singing, ringing girl. Lucas always said I was his muse. But I'd rather be yours, Mr. Orlowski. Oh do write back, dear Mr. Orlowski, and take me on. I'll be a star, promise.

Pygmalion Mâché

Vik Muniz

I can vaguely remember when it started: the first winter after the death of my wife. My lack of social graces had driven even the bugs away and after my retirement from the school, I spent most of my hours alone, sitting in this chair, contemplating the resounding emptiness of this library. I used to dust this place a lot more often than I do now. I would do it alphabetically and because I had to open every volume I cleaned, from Aesopus to Zeno, it would take a full month. Just enough to start all over again. Well, it was during one of my obsessive clean-ups shortly after she died, as I hopelessly tried to maintain this place as she left it, that something entirely instinctive drove my attention to a particular object in the room: This effigy, the stunned ventriloquist's dummy that I fashioned myself in my childhood from papier mâché, perched precariously on the edge of the mantelpiece. We had come a long way and how similarly we had aged. Like me, it had survived the children, the war, the pets, and the constant falls from its place.

I had kept it and repaired it through all those years. Its slight resemblance to my aging self was the mandatory joke and fuel for much laughter during family reunions and visits from friends. Its decrepit presence had finally been integrated into the eclectic decor of the room. It sat there for over forty years, gazing into the void, smiling with the bucolic contempt these puppets generally convey, and all of a sudden, I caught myself smiling back at the damn thing. We sometimes can only notice things after they've been buried in dust. As I sat here to read the Herald or watch the local news, the slightest glance at that blank smile would shatter my concentration and take me back, way back, to those wonderful days of our mutual past:

The toothless smile of my granny Ada when I asked her to make his clothes, the molding of his mouth, the painting of his eyes and the screams of my father after discovering that most of the pulp used to make the dummy had come from his entire Encyclopedia Brittanica.

It occurred to me that the dummy had met everybody I knew, had gone through all the hard and good times Audrey, the girls, and I had gone through, and, as it sat behind my reading chair and facing the TV, I unconsciously had shared with my inane roomer most of the outside information that ever entered this house. It wasn't a coincidence that we were the last ones around; we were the first ones to begin with.

The winter here makes it really hard to get around. Lilian, our youngest, came up only once, bringing along her annoying husband and their dreadful routine of advice: You have to see people, go to the senior center, to the church, make friends, etc. etc. etc. I told them if I had never gone to a church to see God, why would I go to see people? Besides, I hate bingo, cheap talk, and people my age. Deerfield is a cultural desert with lots of traffic jams. I prefer to stay home. They bring me the paper and Audrey's subscription to the Book of the Month. But, between you and me, one can really feel lonely in this neck of the woods. It may seem strange, I confess, but after remembering my complicity with the dummy, I took a lot of comfort in his company. Lilian was right: Old people need people around; what they don't need is to be around people.

I dusted my re-acquainted friend and sat him on the big couch. I read the news to him every morning, and on Thursdays and Saturdays I would sit him in the other chair and together we watched *Masterpiece Theater.* He loved that BBC stuff and so did I. Several times I would leave him in a certain position and would later find him in a different one. Our relationship had grown so intensely that the dummy could no longer be passive or manipulated. He too had a need to exorcise all these years of silence and restraint. He desperately needed help.

One morning, shortly after coffee, I skipped our reading ritual and decided to pick him up and see if his mechanisms were still working. Although my left hand felt awfully tight inside, the rudimentary wire para-phernalia that he had for guts seemed still able to translate the movements of my hand into gesticulations and expressions. His bumpy hands caressed my face and mouth. I was so moved, I couldn't tell for sure which one of us had said thank you. From now on, like an echo, I would hear everything I said, listen to every-thing I read and even have my phone conversations doubled by the soporific voice of the dummy. It sounded a little strange at first but gradually I became quite used to it. Sometimes I would repeat the more difficult words so that he could learn them faster. My demanding friend had such a fondness for dialogue, that I was forced to come out of myself in order to make him happy. In this way we could teach each other to communicate.

In a relatively short time, the dummy's eloquent per-sona was able to fill uninterruptedly the emptiness of my days. We would dedicate entire afternoons to the discussion of cognitive barriers, or to the problematic of ambiguity in the realm of hermeneutics. He would wake me up with a recently found quote from Condillac or Gorgias and recited Luis de Camões until I fell asleep. As his cellulose body found little need for sleep, he would pursue his perspicacious monologue into the night, softly so as not to wake me up. Some-times, this nocturnal mumbling would give me the impression that he talked to me in my dreams.

Having no need for sustenance in any ordinary sense, he fed voraciously on vocabulary, and whatever was ingested remained perpetually present, even in the most pusillanimous sentence he would voice. A basic remark on my clothing would bear the style of Coleridge, a discussion of what to have for supper would recall one day Keats, another, Grosseteste, depending on the menu. Soon enough, his ravenous appetite for words surpassed linguistic barriers; his Homeric Greek and vowel-depleted Arabic consumed the intimacy of our relationship. My inability to keep pace with his learning began to cause problems between us. Desperately, I spent increasing amounts of time immersed in the erudite consumption of language. I would, in one day, spend the entirety of my dismal pension on the purchase of dictionaries and it would still be all in vain; I sat here in this same chair, nearly buried under the *Oxford*, the *Petit Robert*, *Webster's*, *Aurelio*, and even the *Promptorium Pavolorum*. As the puppet's discourse would shift ceaselessly from Boccacio to Laclos, from Goethe to Melville, he would also shift into the languages in which these works were originally written. By the time I would have found the meaning of the word "asymptote" in the *Penguin Dictionary of Psychology*, he would already be quoting William Herschel in relation to Cusanus's *Of Learned Ignorance*.

Unperturbed by my inability to reply to his arguments, he persisted in his abstracting digression at an ominous speed. I, on my side, grew increasingly silent. My pathetic attempts to add anything to what the puppet was saying were invariably rebuffed by much more substantial arguments. I started to see myself pretty much as the puppet used to be. Pretending to understand, I listened to his complexity with the same moronic smile he once had. Well, I did not have much choice; if he noticed my slightest failure to follow his discourse, he immediately attributed it to my hearing. If I didn't respond to what he was saying, he would start talking louder and louder. I did not want the neighbors to think I was going crazy, so I would nod periodically in a jest of approval or smile in awe at the end of certain sentences.

As the situation became increasingly unpleasant, I tried several times to explain the problem to him, but you know how insensitive puppets can be. He would start by acknowledging the problem and then deflect the issue, blaming the order of communication between different systems of being. He would then proceed to find the solution to our problem in the Akkadian verses of Enuma Elish. And worst of all, he would start quoting himself, and me, in every single circumstance in which I quoted him. This impromptu relationship dragged on to the borders of despair until one morning, after being ravaged by Adorno, Confucius and Jameson at the breakfast table, I took advantage of a distracting utterance on *The Timaeus* to pour over his flammable body a whole bottle of my highest proof Haitian rum. Then I lit a match and threw it at him.

Realizing what was happening, the flaming dummy continued his harangue, but this time at a much higher and more desperate pitch. With astonishing speed, he screamed in 98 rpm fragments of *A Thousand and One Nights*, Pascal, Queneau, La Fontaine. He recited Rossetti, Milton, Dryden, Pessoa and finally, after a much slower version of Spinoza in Flemish, he consumed himself in a meaningless mound of ashes. The silence thereafter felt as if the words had risen from the dummy's body and migrated back into things.

Just as this thought crossed my mind, a sudden gust of wind carried away his last remains.

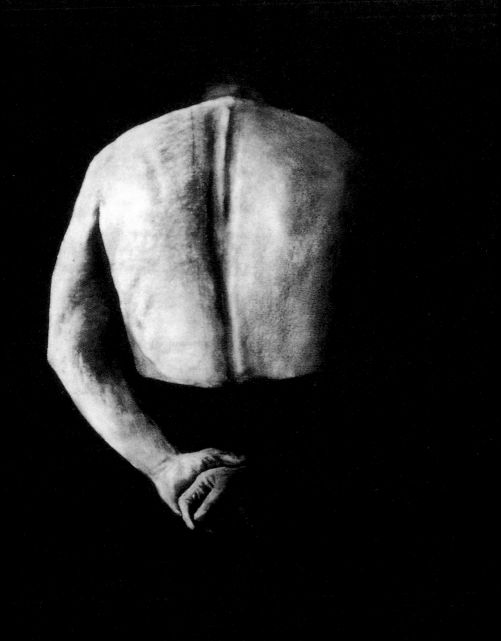

Will It Be A Likeness?

John Berger

(All voices to be spoken by the same man.)

Good Evening. Last week I talked about the dog and we listened to some dogs barking. [Barks.] I suggested that this noise after the aeons of dogs' association with man had something to do with spoken language. Something, but what exactly?

A number of listeners have written me letters—for which I thank you—all of them about the way in which dogs communicate. Some of you sent photos to illustrate your experience.

I gave you my opinion last week [Barks.] that the dog is the only animal with a historical sense of time, but that he can never be a historical agent. He suffers history but he can never make it. And then we looked together at the famous painting by Goya on the subject. And we decided it was better to look at paintings on the radio than on the television. On the TV screen nothing is ever still and this movement stops painting being painting. Whereas on the radio we see nothing but we can listen to silence. And every painting has its own silence.

[Silence.]

A listener from the Black Forest wrote to ask whether, after the dog, we might consider the butterfly, and in particular the *Anthocaris Cardamines*, commonly known as the Fiancée. For this listener—although our principal subject this evening is something altogether different—we have recorded here in the studio the Fiancée in flight. And if you shut the windows and settle in your chair we will now play for you and you will hear the wings of the *Anthocaris Cardamines* beating in flight.

[Silence with atmospheric noises.]

Every butterfly too has its own special silence. For sometimes a sound is more easily grasped as a silence, just as a presence, a visible presence, is sometimes most eloquently conveyed by a disappearance.

[Station noises.]

Who does not know what it is like to go with a friend to a railway station and then to watch the train take them away? [Announcement of departures spoken in Chinese.] As you walk along the platform back into the city, the person who has just gone is often more there, more totally there, than when you embraced them before they climbed into the train. When we embrace to say good-bye, maybe we do it for this reason—to take into our arms what we want to keep when they've gone.

[Telephone rings.]

A listener has just telephoned in to ask me what century in God's name do I think I'm living in?

[Woman's voice over telephone, muffled]. Sounds like the nineteenth!
No, Madame, the one I live in is the sixteenth or the ninth. How many, Madame, do you think were not dark? One in seven?

Today everything everywhere on the planet is for sale.

I'm selling. Here's a back, a man's working back, not yet broken, did I hear an offer?

What would I do with it?

Sell it somewhere where they need backs for work.

[Dog barks.]

Every evening Goya takes his dog for a walk along the Ramblas.

A heart?

How old?

Sixteen and healthy, from Mexico.

OK. Bought.

Then man and dog stroll home and Goya draws the curtains and settles down to look at CNN.

A kidney.

Taken!

One male member and a uterus together.

Together how?

They stayed together. They were chased out of their village, they had no land and they were obliged to sell everything to survive.

I'll take the uterus.

And the male member?

Throw it away, plenty more where he came from.

Difficult—they're inseparable.

NAFTA! Separate them!

I'm not sure…

NAFTA! I tell you!

Nafta?

North American Free Trade Agreement.

No, Madame, I live in this century which I can't say is ours and now, if I may, I shall return to the mystery of what makes a presence.

When all the members have been separated and all the parts sold, what is left?

Something more to sell. A whole is more than the sum of its parts.

Yes, so we sell the personality.

A personality is a media-product and easy to sell.

A presence is the same thing as personality, no?

Presence is not for sale.

If that's true, it's the only thing on this earth that isn't.

A presence has to be given, not bought.

Three hundred girls from Thailand.

I'll take them. Ask Melbourne if he's still interested.

A presence is always unexpected. However familiar. You don't see it coming, it moves in sideways. In this a presence resembles a ghost.

[Dog barks.]

He's let the dog out and the master has gone to sleep.

Once I was in a train traveling to Amsterdam, through Germany, going north following the Rhine. It was a Sunday and I was alone in the compartment and had been traveling for several hours. With me I had a cassette player and so I decided to listen to some music. Beethoven's one-from-last piano sonata. A man stops in the corridor and peers into the compartment. He makes a sign with his hands to enquire if he can open the door. I slide the door open. Come in, I say. He puts a finger to his lips, sits down and slides the door shut. We listen. When the sonata ends, there's only the noise of the train... He's a man of about my age but better dressed and with an attaché case. From it he takes out a sheet of paper, writes some words on it and hands the paper to me. "Thank you," I read, "for allowing me to listen with you." I smile, nod, and know that I should not speak. We sit there silently in the presence of the last movement of the sonata. This is how a presence makes itself felt.

[Beethoven.]

An hour later, when a vendor came down the corridor selling coffee and sandwiches, my traveling companion pointed to what he wanted and I understood how he was dumb, how he could not speak.

[Telephone rings. Muffled voice.] Who was the pianist?

Piotr Andersylwski.

That's not true. Why do you lie?

Because Piotr is a friend of mine. He plays marvelously but he has no means, he came from Poland, he's poor and he's already twenty-six and soon—such is the competition on the concert circuit today—soon it will be too late, forever too late, for him to be recognised for the great pianist he is. So I lied to help him.

On my way here to the radio station this evening I passed a photography shop. In their window they have a notice which says: IDENTITY PHOTOS WITH A TRUE LIKENESS—READY IN TEN MINUTES!

To talk of a likeness is another way of talking of a presence. With photos the question of likeness is incidental. It's merely a question of choosing the likeness you prefer. With a painted or drawn portrait likeness is fundamental; it's not there, there's an absence, a gaping absence.

[Noise of a dog whining and scratching at door.]

The dog is now asking to be let in. The master gets up, opens the door and, instead of returning to bed, goes to his easel on which there is an unfinished painting.

You can't hunt for a likeness. It can escape even a Raphael... Strangely, you can tell whether a likeness is there or not when you've never set eyes on the model or seen any other image of the model. For example, in Raphael's portrait of a woman known as La Muta, the dumb one, there is an astounding likeness. *You can hear it.*

[Silence.]

Whilst in Raphael's double portrait of himself and a friend, painted in 1517, there's no likeness present at all. This time it's a silence without any life in it. Enough to compare this silence with the Fiancée beating her wings, for us to feel the absence.

[Silence.]

You can't set out to trap it. It comes on its own or it doesn't, a likeness. It moves in sideways like a presence. Maybe a likeness *is* a presence.

Are you saying a likeness can't be bought or sold?

No, it can't.

Bad news. Maybe you are lying again?

This time there's no need to lie.

Blah blah blah blah blah blah blah... Pure mystification! If you can't in principle by it or sell it, it doesn't exist. This is what we now know for certain. What you're talking about is your personal phantasm—to which of course you have every right. Without phantasms there would be no consumers, and we'd be back with the apes.

[Animal noise.]

Apes and other animals can feel a presence. When a dog recognises a garment of his master by its smell— perhaps he perceives something similar to a likeness.

So we end up with dogs! I thought we were thinking about invention, creation, human wealth.

One female thyroid gland!

A single thyroid is not sellable. If you're offered one, it's suspect.

There's a painting from Pompeii I'd like to show you all.

Of a dog, I suppose.

No, a woman. She's holding a wooden tablet, like a book, in her left hand and in her right, a pen or stylo, the end of which she holds against her lip. She's thinking about words not yet written. The portrait was painted in the year 79—the year in which the town was buried—and preserved—in lava.

Not a great painting, and if I'm sending it to you by radio—it's simply because it's a likeness. She's here in the studio in front of me, with her fringe just out of curlers and her earrings of golden rings which, as soon as she puts them on, are never still.

A likeness is a gift, something left behind and hidden and later discovered when the house is empty... Whilst hidden, it avoids time.

What do you mean "avoids time?"

Confuses time, if you prefer.

You wouldn't get away with this nonsense on television. TV demands speed and clarity. You can't ramble across the screen as you're rambling right now on the radio.

So I send you the Pompeiian woman of two millennia ago, with the tip of her stylo lightly touching her lower lip and her hands which are not rough with work and never will be. At the most she's twenty years old, and you have the impression of having seen her very recently! [Woman's laughter.] Is that not so?

You are a nostalgic old man!

Or a young romantic?

Anyway they're both finished, they belong to the past. Today we live in a world of exchanges, calculations at the speed of light, credits, debts and winnings.

And the dead don't exist?

Let the dead bury the dead—that was well said and has always been true.

Here's a story about an elusive likeness. I still have a portrait I painted when I was twenty. It's of a woman asleep in a chair and on the table in front of her, in the foreground, there is a bowl of flowers. I was in love with the woman and we lived together in two rooms on the ground floor of a house in London. I think somebody could tell from the painting that I loved her, but there's no likeness there. Her primrose green dress— she made it herself on the table in the room where I painted—has a distinct presence, and her fair hair, in whose colour I always saw green, is striking. But there's no likeness. And until six months ago, if I looked at the painting, I couldn't refind a likeness in my memory either. If I shut my eyes, I saw her. But I couldn't see her sitting in the chair in her green dress.

Six months ago I happened to be in London and I found myself two minutes' walk away from the modest house where we rented the two rooms. The house had been done up and repainted but it hadn't been rebuilt. So I knocked on the door. A man opened it and I explained that fifty years ago I had lived there and would it be possible for me to see the two rooms on the ground floor?

He invited me in. He and his wife occupied the whole house. There were carpets and lamps and paintings and china plates on the walls and a hi-fi and silver trays. Useless to look for the gas meter which we fed with coins when we were cold and needed to light the gas-fire or heat some water. Useless to look for the bathtub which when we weren't taking a bath served as a sup-port for a tabletop on which we chopped onions and beat eggs. Everything had been replaced and nothing was the same except for the plaster mouldings on the ceiling and the proportions of the large window by whose light she made her clothes and I painted.

I asked if I could draw back the curtains. And I stood there staring at the window panes—it was raining and already evening so I could see nothing outside.

There I found her likeness as she sat in the chair asleep in the green dress.

Likenesses hide in rooms, you find them sometimes when they're being emptied.

There are many people who are secluded: They live in a kind of Switzerland of perception so that they can't see a likeness when it's staring them in the face.

A journalist is visiting a modern prison which is the pride of the local authorities. They call it a model prison. The journalist is chatting with a long-term prisoner. Finally, still taking notes, he asks, "And what did you do before?"

"Before what?"

"Before you were here."

The prisoner stares at him.

"Crime," he says, "crime…"

[Dog barks.]

It is a new day, and Goya is taking the dog for a walk. They are both in exile. In the town of Bordeaux which, when there is a west wind, smells of the Atlantic.

As the Nikkei Stock Average breaks through the 2000-point mark, European money managers brim with confidence that the market to watch next year will be Japan.

An eye with a perfect retina, going, going, gone.

In these parts it is a miracle the people are still alive, says Moisés, a young man who has joined the Zapatista insurrection in Chiapas, south-east Mexico. "Families of seven to twelve people have been surviving on a hectare or half a hectare of infertile soil… We have nothing, absolutely nothing, no decent roof over our heads, no land, no work, no health, no food, no education…" The year is 1994.

Now I'm going to send you by radio a strange likeness—that of a man whose face we do not know.

Whenever he's in company, he wears a black ski mask. "Here we are," he says, "the forever-dead, dying once again, but now in order to live." His assumed name is Marcos. Subcommandante Insurgente Marcos.

A terrorist! It was agreed that this was a radio talk about economics, and you contrive to introduce a terrorist.

An expert in violence!

He's manipulating you at this moment.

[Telephone rings.]

Don't answer it!

I'm not defending him, I'm just transmitting his likeness. A likeness created by his own words:

"I have the urge to write to you and tell you something about being 'the professionals of violence' as we have so often been called. Yes, we are professionals. But our profession is hope...out of our spent and broken bodies must rise up a new world... Will we see it? Does it matter? I believe that it doesn't matter as much as knowing with undeniable certainty that it will be born, and that we have put our all—our lives, bodies and souls—into this long and painful but historic birth. *Amor y dolor*—love and pain: two words that not only rhyme, but join up and march together."

Empty leftist rhetoric!

Here is the rest of his likeness.

"There is something else about this passionate moving of words, something that does not appear in any postscript or any communiqué. It is the anxiety, the uncertainty, the galloping questions that assault us every time one of the couriers leaves with one, or several, communiqués. Questions and more questions fill up our nights, accompany us on our rounds to check the guards, sit beside us on some broken tree trunk looking at the food on the plate… 'Were these words the best ones to say what we wanted to say?' 'Were they the right words at this time?' 'Were they understandable?'"

A likeness is a gift and remains unmistakable—even when hidden behind a mask.

A likeness can be effaced. Today Che Guevara sells T-shirts, that's all that is left of his likeness.

Are you sure?

[Silence.]

Sure?

[Silence.]

Why don't you say something? Silence, you know, is something you can't censor, and there are circumstances in which silence becomes subversive, that's why you have to fill it with noise all the while.

There's something dark about the silence around music, marvelously dark.

Goya is walking with his dog by the ocean.

The other day I was listening to Glenn Gould playing Mozart's Fantasy in C. Moll. I'm not going to put it on for you, for if I did, I'd have nothing more to say, and they'd pay me less for this programme and I need the money to pay a dentist's bill. Nevertheless I want to remind you of how Gould plays. *He plays like one of the already-dead come back to the world to play its music.* That's how he played when he was alive.

Three nimble hands.

Why three?

One of the women had an accident at work.

Bought.

[Dog barks.]

In your world there are no likenesses—which is why you want to buy them and can't.

Whose dog is it?

I'll tell you the story of the best likeness ever made. John is the only one who tells the story. The other Evangelists don't refer to it—though they refer to Martha and Mary. The two sisters had a brother, Lazarus, who fell sick and died in the village of Bethany. When Jesus, who was a friend of the family, arrived in the village, Lazarus had been dead and buried for four days.

"Where have you laid him?" he asked.

"Come and see, Lord," they replied.

Jesus wept.

Then the Jews said: "See how he loved him!"

But some of them said: "Could not he, who opened the eyes of the blind man, have kept this man from dying?"

Jesus, once more deeply moved, came to the tomb. It was a cave with a stone laid across the entrance. "Take away the stone," he said.

So they took away the stone.

Jesus called in a loud voice. "Lazarus, Come out!" The dead man came out, his hands and feet wrapped with strips of linen and a cloth round his face.

Jesus said to them: "Take off the grave clothes and let him go."

This is the story of the perfect likeness. And it provoked Caiaphas, the high priest, to lay the plot for the taking of Jesus's own life.

Goya is going back with his dog to work in his studio.

Next week I propose to talk about laughter, and as a way of introducing the subject, I'll sign off now by playing you a tape made by my friend Geoff Dyer:

[Jazz on tape.]

Yeah, hello John. That was music from Don Cherry who died yesterday which was all very sad ... and I put that on because he's obviously somebody who, in his life and his playing, knew no frontiers and obviously that's the same for you and also that's why I'm going to read a short bit from your new book:

"Jean Ferrero is seated at a café table under the ocher arcades in the Via Po. In front of him is a cappuccino and a glass of ice-cold water. Nothing else in the city sparkles like these glasses of water. He leans back in his chair; he has crossed the mountains. Probably his grandfather once came to Torino to argue a case with a notary. Today the arcades are the colour of old files whose labels have been changed many times. Hearing a laugh, he raises his head. It takes him some time to find the one laughing. It's a woman's laugh. Not in the arcade, not at the bar, not by the newspaper kiosk. The laughter sounds as if it comes from a field in the country. Then he spots her. She is standing at a second-storey window on the other side of the street, shaking a tablecloth or a bedcover. A tram passes but he still hears her laughter, and she is still laughing when the tram has gone, a woman no longer young, with heavy arms and short hair. It is impossible to know what she's laughing at. When she stops laughing, she'll have to sit down to catch her breath."

[Silence.]

Turn the volume of the silence up and you'll hear snowflakes falling on deep snow...

The last likeness...

Tabula Rasa

Luc Sante

Somehow he wound up in the custody of suite 3719 of some unnamed Marriott Intercontinental in some unknown burg, Brussels or Jakarta or Dallas-Fort Worth. He knew the number because there was a key-card on the credenza on which the number had been scrawled in ballpoint pen, contrary to security advice. The key-card had been left there as a taunt, he figured, because it was of no use whatever. Not only couldn't he open the hallway door from the inside, he couldn't find it. Every door in the suite led to a closet or the bathroom or connected the sitting-room with the bedroom. His first move was to look around the rooms, furnished but resolutely bare of specifics except for the key-card, and then his second act was to open every door, looking for the hallway door. Nonplussed, he then thought to look out a window, only there were no windows, either.

He became aware of his surroundings the way he might have noticed that clouds were gathering overhead. That is, he noticed gradually, as if he had been concentrating on something else, shop windows or conversation or a book. He did not have a sensation of coming to, as if from sleep or unconsciousness. On the other hand, he couldn't recall just what he had been engaged in before he became aware of his surroundings. He hadn't been reading; the room contained no texts, not a bible or a brochure or a room-service menu, as he determined when, after he gave up looking for a window, he opened every drawer and cabinet door, finding nothing, no object of any description.

He certainly hadn't been talking, either. There was no telephone in the suite. He supposed he might have been talking to himself, but he rarely did that out loud, even during long periods of solitude, which were fairly frequent in his life. He might possibly have been lost in thought—this sometimes did occur, causing him to miss his bus stop or trip over things in the street. But then he would have some recollection of his surroundings as they were when he initially plunged into his meditation. What, then, were his last memories?

Of course, depicting his mental processes in this fashion would make it sound as if he had looked around, looked for a door, looked for a window, looked for a clue, and then, unsatisfied but determined, had sat down and begun to ratiocinate. While this is indeed what happened, at least in outline form, it omits first his panic, and then his violence. After he had looked around, and after he had opened all the doors, he opened all the doors again, and then he opened them all again, and then again, and then again. And then he opened them all again. He paused, went to a corner, and propped his head in the crook of the two walls, and then he went and opened them all again. He started moving furniture, looking behind chairs as if there might be some kind of mouse-door concealed behind them, and then he shunted aside the drapes. He broke a fingernail trying to pry up an end of the carpet to see if there might be a trap door underneath, but he didn't succeed. Then he paused. He went to move but he couldn't because he was caught in the center of the sitting-room, poised for some decisive action, such as the opening of a door, but there was no door which was the right door, so he was left frozen, one foot in front of the other, slightly off-balance. Then he moved to the bedroom and stood in its center, repeating his sequential loop of immobility. And that is when he panicked.

When he began looking for a window, he was fully aware that he had inspected every inch of the premises while looking for a door, and that he had not encountered any windows in his peregrinations. He had a passing thought that had he seen a window, he would have remembered it, he would have taken in some note of light or sky or traffic, but no such signpost stood in his head. So by the time he began looking for a window, he was already acting contrary to reason. He was simply darting around in hurried and redundant motion. After some time spent wearing a groove in the carpets from room to room, he began attacking the suite. He tore down the drapes, barely pausing to register the fact that they served no actual purpose. He threw chairs around, he stripped the bed, he took the pictures off the wall and flung them across the room, he pounded his fists against the walls, the door, the floor. He tried in vain to bring down the sprinkler pipes discreetly suspended from the ceiling. He perspired heavily.

Then he sat down, and his heart rate gradually slowed, although it could not truly be said to have returned to normal. He willed it to slow down, breathing deeply, forcing all the air out of his lungs at each exhalation and making the inhalations measured and gradual. After some time spent breathing carefully and looking at his shoes, he was ready to look for some other clue to his situation. It was then that he opened all the drawers and cabinet doors and found nothing. Or nothing that could answer his question, anyway. He did find, in the bathroom, tiny wrapped cakes of soap, and small bottles of shampoo and body lotion, and a cardboard envelope containing a shower cap, and a comb, and a chamois cloth, and a shoehorn, all of them branded with a logotype formed of the letters "M I", which is what led him to surmise that he was in a hotel of the Marriott Intercontinental chain, although he then began to wonder whether Marriott and Intercontinental were not in fact two separate chains, quite independent of each other. The letters M and I were superimposed, anyway, so that the acronym might have been either IM or MI—Internal Medicine or Murder Incorporated.

In the bedroom he had previously neglected a small refrigerator, which contained a fully-stocked minibar. Whiskey and brandy, vodka and gin, beer and wine, Coca-Cola and Fanta, mineral water sparkling and flat, pretzels and potato chips, chocolates and gummy bears. He drank a tiny bottle of single-malt scotch, and chased it with a slightly larger bottle of sparkling mineral water. While ingesting the latter he looked at its label, which featured snow-capped peaks towering over a lake surrounded by evergreens. A family of deer stood to one side, apparently surprised while grazing. An eagle soared overhead. The sky was clear blue, with a decorative couple of fleecy cumulus clouds parked at the eleven and two o'clock positions. Above this edenic scene were printed the words MINERAL WATER. No brand name, no source of origin, no bottling-plant location. He threw the bottle at the wall, which dented slightly under the impact of the glass, but the bottle didn't break.

When he looked just past the spot on the wall dented by the impact of the bottle, he noticed one of the pictures he had torn down. It was a reproduction of a painting, which featured peaks, a lake, evergreens, deer, an eagle, clouds. It was exactly the same as the label on the bottle, minus its title. He stood and continued his inventory of pictures: day lilies in a vase against a blue background; a sunset over the sea; a mare and her colt cavorting in a field; a sailboat riding the wind with its mast canted at a 60° angle; two Siamese kittens batting at a ball of yellow yarn. He looked behind each of the pictures: no framer's label. He looked under each of the chairs: no tags or inscriptions of any sort. He upended the mattress and inspected its edges all the way around: again nothing. Besides the obvious lack of egress, another curious absence had vaguely registered in his mind, and now he realized what it was: no television. There was no clock, either. There was no state-mandated fire-escape route or room tariff as established by law framed and bolted to the inside of a door. He possessed a single clue as to his surroundings—the words MINERAL WATER were printed in English—but that might be true in nearly any part of the world these days. The labels on the other contents of the minibar were also in English, and similarly non-specific otherwise. The scotch was called "Old Grouse", the brandy was called "Duke's Estate", the vodka was called "Winter Palace", the gin was called "London Bridge", the wine was called "Chateau Dupont", the beer was called "Munich's Best". The edible substances were all produced by a firm called Ace. Their weights were all indicated in grams, but that was equally meaningless.

When he had satisfied himself that his search had been exhaustive, he began trying to recall his last memories before he became aware of his surroundings. All he could remember was his daily routine: the shower, the solitary breakfast, the wait for the bus, the lecture to pimply graduate students on medieval papacies and their theological impact, the somnolence over Latin commentaries in his library carrel, the wait for the bus, the solitary supper, the hours of television. Was he on vacation? he wondered wildly. Perhaps he had taken a package, an airfare-hotel deal. Perhaps he was in Cozumel. He had no memory of having been kidnapped, no image of burly figures assaulting him and tying him up. He apparently had no luggage, he noted. He was wearing a charcoal raincoat, a glen-plaid suit, a light blue shirt, a maroon and black striped tie, black socks, and black oxfords. Suddenly inspired, he went through his pockets. No money, no keys, no address book, no credit cards, no memo pad, no watch. Nothing, in fact, but a white pencil. A white pencil? He could only associate it with the sixty-color set he had once received as a Christmas present. Then he sat, glazed.

He sat for what might have been a very long time. It might just as well have been a very short time, since there was no way of measuring. As he sat, he continued to comb his memory, but to no avail. He made an effort to keep himself very still and listened for ambient sounds. He heard only a vague hum, as if from a heating system. He eventually fell asleep. He dreamed of nothing. When he awoke, he was ravenous. He consumed a bag of pretzels and one of potato chips, and drank a beer. No sooner had he completed his meal than he realized that he had ingested a quarter of his entire supply of food. This thought prompted another burst of panic, but the succeeding realization that there was nothing he could do about it calmed him. Fatalism made him sleepy. He had been sleeping sitting up, propped against a wall of the bedroom, and now he removed his raincoat, jacket, tie, belt, and shoes, and stretched out on the mattress, wrapping himself in a blanket.

When he awoke he considered his situation. He had a bit of food, and liquids galore, if he added the tap water—possibly dense with impurities, but the hazard seemed minor, overall. He was warm. He had sufficient light. He had air, for all that it felt a bit secondhand, like the air in airplanes. When he ran out of food, he could perhaps eat his shoes and his belt, and maybe the sofa in the sitting-room was made of leather, rather than vinyl, so he could eat that, too. Provided he could digest the stuff, it would last him a fair amount of time. His principal task, then, was to keep himself from becoming insane. He remembered reading accounts of prisoners kept in solitary confinement, how they kept their wits together over years of sensory deprivation by playing games of chess in their heads, but he had never been any good at chess, and couldn't even remember the rules very well. Then there were those who traveled mentally, making themselves conduct voyages in real time, enumerating every detail of, say, a bicycle journey through France, or a trip by canoe through the tributaries of the Mississippi from New Orleans to the Yukon. He could make a stab at it, he supposed, although the only route he was terribly familiar with was the one on the number seven bus from his corner to the university and back. He could mentally travel that road with ease and detail, but it only took about twenty minutes. He could, he supposed, recite numerous papal bulls and council summaries in their entirety, although sometimes, even in happier circumstances, he feared that such fare would drive him mad unassisted.

But he required activity, and he also needed order. So he set about returning all the objects he had flung about to their proper places. He rehung all the pictures on their appropriate hooks. He made the bed, and for once in his life became stringent about doing it correctly, forcing himself to redo it several times until he had achieved perfect hospital corners. He replaced the chairs in their original positions, guided by the imprints their feet had left in the carpets. He refastened the shower curtain to its rings, noting with a bit of pride that he hadn't smashed the mirror or the water glasses, or damaged the plumbing. When he had finished, he inspected his surroundings with a slightly proprietary air, as if he were Robinson Crusoe and he had just built himself a cabin and a latrine in the jungle, using available materials. Then he took off all his clothes and ran a bath. He made it very hot, so that he could only enter it by slow degrees. Then he sat in it and emptied his mind as best he could. He felt himself wilt. When at length he removed the plug, he halfway expected that he would run down the drain.

He dried himself with one of the capacious, unmonogrammed towels, then he wrapped it around his middle like a sarong. He sat on the bed. Then he sat on the sofa in the sitting-room, and bent down and sniffed it, happily satisfying himself that it was indeed leather. Then he sat on each of the chairs, in turn. He gave each of the chairs a name, as if they were pets. Roscoe and Boris were in the sitting-room, and Molly and Pearl were in the bedroom. He decided not to name the sofa, since he would eventually eat it. He sat on the floor, and then he lay down on it. He entered each of the closets, noticing the hangers, the shoe rack, the extra blanket, the folding suitcase stand for the first time. He noticed, too, the electrical cord that ran back into a hole in the far wall, and briefly considered starting a fire, but then he reflected that he would be its first victim. Anyway, he now had a suicide pill, but he resolved to put such thoughts out of his mind for the present. He resolved to be happy. He was alive and in the world, cosseted by creature comforts. The poor and homeless could only dream of circumstances like his. A suite of this size and appointment would cost, what, $400 a night in most places, much higher in resort areas and the major metropolitan districts.

He now needed a new task. He thought of rearranging the furniture, but its deployment seemed so perfect already. He did some push-ups and some sit-ups, but the exercise bored him. He removed all the cushions from the chairs and the sofa and hunted around in the cracks for lost coins, but he failed to find so much as a paper clip. He counted the repetitions of the floral pattern on the wallpaper in the sitting-room, he counted the tiles in the bathroom. He began counting the threads in the carpeting, but then he became dizzy and had to stop. He unscrewed and rescrewed all the light-bulbs, employing a washcloth to keep from burning his hand. He tried to play make-believe. He pretended he was a businessman, having closed a giant deal here in Tokyo, and the image sparked to life but then burned out immediately. Then he pretended he was a tourist in Rio, planning the next day's activities, but he couldn't remember all that much of what he'd read about Rio. Would he go to a bullfight? The image erased itself. Then he was a rock star, relaxing after the set in Stockholm, awaiting the arrival of the groupies. But he was all too aware of his flabby middle, his dead white skin with its pathetic red hairs, his knock-knees, his sagging shoulders. That image, too, collapsed.

Then he remembered the white pencil. He possessed a tool. Excitedly he brought it forth from the inside pocket of his suitcoat. He had no paper, but there were walls. But the white wouldn't show against the beige. He tried the closet doors, which were imitation mahogany, but the pencil failed to register on their varnished surfaces. He flailed around, looking for a sufficiently dark and matte surface. He thought of altering the pictures, but their color schemes were uniformly bright, and on the pale end of the spectrum. The chairs were beige, the bedding was predominantly white, the bathroom and its contents were uniformly white. Then he saw his raincoat. He made an experimental scribble. It showed beautifully on the charcoal cloth, like chalk on a blackboard. He thought of writing, but any text—his life story, perhaps—would rapidly cover the entire surface. He would have to draw. He hadn't drawn in many years, but he had shown talent as a child. He began drawing a face. It looked stupid, a bad cartoon. A house, a tree, a flower appeared likewise. He could only draw from life, as he remembered from his art lessons. His subject matter was set, then. He would have to draw his new home. Carefully, he tore the raincoat along its seams, and then, using his teeth, into a pile of smallish rectangles. He positioned himself in the bedroom, just outside the doorway, at a $45°$ angle to the sitting-room. He pulled up a chair and began to sketch.

The Story of Estraperlo

Quico Rivas

"You are Mr. Rivas, I believe? My name is Thomas Perl. May I offer you a drink?"

I answered with a cordial gesture and invited the stranger to join me at my table. He didn't just sit down, he collapsed onto a wicker chair that groaned piteously. Mr. Perl was solidly built, with limp, ash-colored hair. He had a florid complexion, a pointy nose, thin lips, and bulging eyes. A tracery of fine red veins over his nose and cheeks betrayed him as a habitual drinker. He ordered a fourteen-year-old unblended Scotch with lots of ice. I decided to follow suit.

"You see, Mr. Rivas, I am—how shall I say?—retired." I had not noticed anything in his hands before, when he sat down, but as he spoke, Mr. Perl toyed continuously with a deck of cards. "I have an obligation, a commitment I made to myself. The fact is, I'm going to write a book."

Well, well, I thought, the usual nut who feels the time has come for him to tell the world the story of his insignificant life. Nevertheless—I don't know why—I'd taken a liking to the man. Judging by his compulsive attachment to his cards, I assumed that he must be a retired gambler. When I considered that the memoirs of poker or roulette players were not among the worst examples of the genre, I decided to grant Mr. Perl the same degree of indulgence that I, as a writer, confer upon myself.

"You have a perfect right to become an author, Mr. Perl. Look at me: I'm a professional writer, but I'm thinking of opening a bar."

Mr. Perl smiled, seeming somewhat relieved, and went on ceremoniously, in a correct, fluent Spanish. His vague Central European accent was dotted here and there with South American resonances.

"As you well know, Mr. Rivas, in all languages there are words, nouns, adjectives, even verbs that derive from the names of people and that form part of everyday speech. Kafkaesque, for instance."

"Quixotic," I suggested, just to show the flag.

"Exactly, exactly. I see you get my point." Mr. Perl had taken a small notebook out of his jacket pocket and was leafing through it. The cards seemed to have vanished.

At that moment, an elderly English couple—the man tall and stiff, the woman short and stout—walked into the bar and took a table at the opposite end. During the winter season, the English colony held the majority on the Illa D'Or. In an instant, Mr. Costa, the hotel's proprietor and excellent bartender, was wielding the cocktail shaker, making them two of his famous dry martinis. As if relaxed by the rhythmic rattling of the shaker, Mr. Perl—a person whom I could see was susceptible to reveries—continued. "My last name entered Spanish fifty years ago, exactly fifty—not one more, not one less. And it did so, I must admit, rather ignominiously. This has been very painful for me, for which reason I have decided to dedicate what life I have left to the task of redeeming my name."

"I'm curious, Mr. Perl," I answered as I mentally reviewed Spanish words deriving from the root *perl*—the only one that came to me was "perla," a bit flashy perhaps as a surname but hardly outrageous enough to justify so much indignation. "Could you be more explicit?"

"*Chanchullo!*" answered Mr. Perl, with a grimace of rage. "Trickery! That, along with other charming things, is what my last name came to mean in Spanish. *Chanchullo!* Do you know a more disagreeable, more ignoble, more…more..?"

"Of course, it isn't a pretty word, but I don't really see the relationship between *chanchullo* and Perl."

Mr. Perl placed his notebook on the table. As if by magic, the deck of cards reappeared in his right hand. He began to shuffle with the speed and skill of a professional cardsharp. Handling them seemed to calm him down. I remained silent, observing. Cards have always had a mesmerizing effect on me, too.

After a few moments, the deck disappeared up his sleeve. "Excuse me, Mr. Rivas," he said. "Just habits that have stayed with me from the old days. I assure you, I stopped playing cards long ago. The truth is that for many years I haven't played anything."

The situation was beginning to get embarrassing. My companion seemed to be one of those people caught in a tangle of memories they can't express. "May I offer you one of Mr. Costa's famous dry martinis?" I suggested, hoping to lighten his mood.

But Mr. Perl was a man of fixed ideas. He ordered another malt whiskey and, after a good-sized swallow, seemed to recover a bit. Then, slowly, in a confidential tone, savoring each syllable as if he were sharing a huge secret with me, he said: "*Estraperlo*, that's the word, *es-tra-per-lo*. What does that say to you?"

"If I remember correctly, the people who practiced *estraperlo* were unscrupulous businessmen and smugglers during the postwar years, when everything was being rationed. They made deals on the black market for essential items: coffee, sugar, medicine, nylons... When I was just a boy, I remember..."

"Exactly, exactly," Mr. Perl interrupted me. "*Chanchullo*. Intrigue. That is what you call it now. A very... popular word, but it is a young word. I am old enough to remember 1935, the birth—if you can put it that way— of the wretched expression to which you refer. You will not realize this, but the term resulted from the fusion of the first syllables in the last names of my deceased father, Thomas Perl, and his partner, Daniel Strauss."

"A curious case, it certainly is."

"A unique case, Mr. Rivas. Words derived from the fusion of proper nouns—there can be very few in any language. But one derived from two foreign names, you can bet this is a unique and unrepeatable case. According to the official story, my father and his partner came to be, if not the cause…how to put it…then the catalyst of your civil war."

"For God's sake!"

Mr. Perl fixed his glassy eyes on mine. A twisted smile crossed his lips.

"It's a long story."

"I'm all ears."

"We could take a walk; it's a delightful afternoon."
The afternoon was indeed splendid, with that silvery glow some December afternoons have. But the sea looked a bit rough, whipped by a light westerly breeze, and in the distance, at the far end of the bay, above the foothills of Malpas, Las Caletas, and Punta Negra, heavy clouds were gathering.

As we strolled along the pine-studded path parallel to the beach, Mr. Perl filled in his curious story.

His father, Thomas Perl Sr., a Jew of Austrian origin, left his homeland when he was very young, to seek his fortune. Although he'd been a promising mathematics student in Vienna, he had to make his way in the New World by taking on the most menial of jobs. In Las Vegas, that cement and neon mirage founded in the desert just a short time before, the young and enterprising Thomas Perl Sr. found a fertile territory that accommodated both his thirst for adventure and his mathematical passion. He didn't do too badly. He worked as a croupier and later became a professional gambler. In one way or another, he managed to keep himself afloat. He was neither a superstitious nor a visceral player, but what is usually understood as a systematic gambler. One of those cold, patient, meticulous types, who does not get intoxicated with the rustle of cards on the table or the heart-pounding skip of the steel ball over the spokes of the roulette wheel, but who, rather, seems intent on the abstruse piles of numbers he conscientiously records in his notebook, one who gives himself over to complicated computations of probabilities in an urge to find the system—The System—that will allow him to subvert the inexorable laws of chance.

"Believe me, Mr. Rivas, those systems are not always as hare-brained as people think," said Mr. Perl, taking advantage of a pause in our walk. He looked out over the bay, where the sun still glinted through the gathering clouds. "Sometimes they work in specific cases, very

specific cases, and for very short periods, too short...
I'm speaking from personal experience."

Be that as it may, the fact is that during the twenties,
Thomas Perl Sr. learned how to administer his winnings and spread his losses.

"Chance decided that in 1929, the very year of the
stock-market crash, my father fell in love with the
woman who would become my mother. They married
and went on a long trip though Europe and South
America. They ended up in Mexico, where I was born.
Which is why I have both Mexican nationality and a
Mexican passport."

When he asked for her hand in marriage, Thomas Perl
Sr. solemnly promised his wife that his life would change.
According to his son, he kept his promise up to a point,
though in a very curious way. Away from casinos and
dedicated to business, he nevertheless remained ob-
sessed with inventing, if not a system, then a machine
for abolishing chance. In the garage of his house in
Mexico, he set up a workshop where he locked himself
away in his spare time. It took him two years to con-
struct the prototype of a very special roulette table, a
table where risk and accident were balanced by calculation and the player's abilities. A contraption that,
while conserving all the external traits of a game of
chance, would not be classified as such by the agencies
responsible for regulating such devices.

That detail was, no doubt, what attracted the attention of a character who intruded into the life of the Perl family. His name was Daniel Strauss—allegedly also a Jew who had settled in Mexico, but of Dutch origin—a skillful speculator, a schemer with captivating manners and overwhelming charm who knew how to cheat the foolish.

Daniel Strauss and Thomas Perl Sr. founded a company to market the new game, patented under the name of Straperlo. Strauss, who had a worldwide network of political and financial contacts, was in charge of introducing and promoting the product. It is not clear why he cast his eye on Spain. Perhaps here he could count on good friends in the highest circles; also, he probably supposed that insofar as gambling was concerned this was virgin territory—games of chance had been prohibited many years before—a nation thirsty for and favorable to any kind of risk. If he knew how to play his hand, the fragile and unstable Second Republic offered him more than enough space to manoeuver among the incestuous interests of a political class traditionally open to bribes and corruption.

Daniel Strauss and the Perl family moved to Spain at the end of 1934. While Strauss dedicated himself to establishing contacts with impresarios and politicians by travelling continuously back and forth between Madrid and Barcelona, the Perl family installed itself in the north of Mallorca as guests of Ramón Ramouge, an old friend from Buenos Aires.

Ramouge's was a refined world, sensual and decadent. "He never gave a thought to expense," Mr. Perl said nostalgically. "Like all South American millionaires, he was a spendthrift and given to ostentation. He brought in architects and artists from all over the world, and they built him a delirious architectural pastiche, a futurist version of the Aztec pyramids and the hanging gardens of Babylon. Ramouge gave endless magnificent parties, Pantagruelesque banquets, authentic bacchanals where the richest and most chic people on the planet would gather. Aristocrats, movie stars, scientists, celebrated painters, sportsmen, bankers, dandies, and, of course, all the snobs, fortune hunters, and professional beauties who follow the scent of money. Today all that seems a cliché, but it really was that way. People played tennis, danced the fox-trot, worshipped fast cars and anything that sounded even vaguely new. Novelty was the authentic passion, and people fervently argued about fashion, motorcars, art, literature...anything except politics.

"Ramouge's intimate friend was Adam Diehl, another Argentine millionaire who bought half the Formentor peninsula. He invested his fortune in building the most modern and luxurious hotel in the Mediterranean. It was located in an extraordinarily beautiful setting, which could only be reached by sea or on a tortuous mule trail. Adam Diehl was involved in the scandal of "Straperlo" too, and his end was very sad. The war ruined him completely. He didn't even have enough money to get back to his own country, and a collection was taken up in the village of Pollença to buy him a ticket.

"The civil war wiped that unreal, unrepeatable world off the map. My family and I fled just before the military uprising, and this is the first time I have been back to the island since. Mr. Costa tells me that the war was very short in Mallorca. The nationalists took over in a few days. The forces of the left barely offered any resistance. Many were executed. The foreign colony—what survived of it—was allowed to stay on, but not their goods and properties. The Ramouge estate was expropriated by the navy, which built the military base alongside our hotel. The mansion itself was never used; it was simply sealed up. Ramouge and his family were only allowed to take a couple of suitcases."

By then, the sun had set below the horizon. Unlike other days, instead of a fan of brilliant pinks and scarlets, the sky was densely overcast. The temperature continued to drop, and the breeze had become a strong wind.

"*Sic transit gloria mundi*, Mr Perl, but meanwhile, allow me to suggest a lobster dinner in the restaurant of the Nautical Club."

Between Cala Fornels, in the southern part of Menorca, and Cape Formentor, in the north of Mallorca, grow the best lobsters in the world. While the waiters in the restaurant chattered about the approaching storm, Mr. Perl—whose ease in passing from gloom to joviality continued to surprise me—required only one glass of good Rioja to pick up the most elusive thread of his story, that is, the adventures of Daniel Strauss, whom we'd abandoned quite a while ago conspiring all over Spain.

It seems that Strauss made his first contacts in Barcelona, where he managed to arouse interest in the Straperlo among several relevant figures connected to the left-wing Radical Party, among them Alejandro Lerroux, the famous Republican politician who'd survived a thousand battles. Don Alejandro, who persisted in using the "Don," even though he was the son of a humble veteran, was, along with Thomas Perl Sr., the other sacrificial lamb in this story. He deserves, therefore, our attention.

An ambitious and self-taught politician, an energetic and astute man, with few or no scruples in matters of morality or ideology, endowed by nature with a great histrionic talent and fiery oratory, Don Alejandro Lerroux had been, since the end of the last century, elevated to the first rank of Spanish politics. A demagogue and a populist, the demons of his political campaigns were the Monarchy and the Catholic Church, to which he ascribed all the evils of the nation, and which he opposed in the name of what was then called the "moral regeneration" of the country. The Radical Party, which he founded and over which he exercised a permanent and absolute control, was an efficient electoral and propaganda machine, modern, very well-oiled, and capable of guaranteeing him ample popular support, especially among the lower-middle and upper-middle classes.

As he grew older, Alejandro Lerroux—a pragmatic politician who knew how to flow with the tides—cooled down the incendiary tone of his youthful anti-clerical, anti-Catalan rhetoric. After the fall of the Monarchy and the proclamation of the Second Republic, he began to smell power, and the tone of his speeches became more right-wing and authoritarian. He proclaimed himself a protector of the Catholic Church and of private property, a supporter of the death penalty and of maintaining public order at all costs. Many who had once feared him began to see him as the only Republican politician on the right capable of facing up to the growing waves of attacks, disturbances, and savage strikes promoted by the revolutionary parties and the unions.

So, this was Alejandro Lerroux: for some a proud Republican lion and for others a cynical operetta radical; a physical and political heavyweight; a man with an extraordinary biography who had survived police persecution, jail, trials, exiles, and duels. This expert deceiver of the masses had no personal fortune, but always played the grand gentleman, so that his numerous creditors would end up being unable to resist making him a new loan, happy in the assumption that they had just spoken with the man who would save Spain. This perfect example of the self-made man, who was never known to have a regular income, came to be a great friend and collaborator of Juan March, "the pirate of the Mediterranean", the Mallorcan smuggler who became the richest man in Spain, and who, paradoxically, personally financed the military uprising against the Republic.

For Don Alejandro Lerroux, the great moment came toward the end of 1933, when he was about to turn sixty. After some hotly disputed elections, in which the right-wing Republican parties triumphed easily over the Socialist-Republican coalition of the left, the now-centrist Radical Party, garnering almost one hundred deputies, came in second. Don Alejandro had finally realized his life-long dream, and received from the President of the Republic instructions to form a government. But not even one year had passed when this same Don Alejandro Lerroux, at the height of his career, found himself forced to present his irrevocable resignation and to witness the painful spectacle of his party's collapse and the ignominious end of his political career, due to a monumental scandal the press baptized "The Straperlo Affair."

"From what I've read and researched until now, which is not a great deal," confessed Mr. Perl as he finished off the legs of his lobster, "I deduce that no one has taken the trouble to clearly document what really happened. It was a seemingly insignificant matter, but it came to acquire enormous magnitude. I believe in the existence of chance in every level of life except politics. In politics, nothing happens by chance."

According to Mr. Perl's analysis, the sequence of events that transpired because of Lerroux's resignation is what made possible, first, the triumph of the Popular Front in the general elections and, as a result of this, the rejection of democracy by a good part of the forces of the right wing and its subsequent support of the Fascist military uprising.

"With Lerroux still in government, his 'friend' Juan March, the greatest 'estraperlist' in history, would never have placed his immense fortune at the service of the Fascists. Lerroux had to be put out of commission, but at the same time this fatal blow to him would have to be dealt in such a way as to respect March's allies in the Government.

"If the Straperlo—the root of the scandal that followed—hadn't existed, someone would have had to invent it. As far as I know, no one has ever really explained the damned contraption. It's assumed to be a fraud, a kind of rigged roulette; however, no one describes the trick or explains the fraud, not even how it worked. Besides, the substance of the scandal had to do not with the supposedly fraudulent nature of the machine but with the bribes paid by its promotor. Not its inventor, you'll notice—not my father—but the man whom everyone in the press and in Parliament, aloud or in print, began to call 'the Jew Strauss'. And, I wonder, who devised the plot? Who pulled the strings? I don't want to abuse your patience, Mr. Rivas, so I'll only add that to answer those questions you'd have to ask who the primary beneficiaries would be. And the answer is: the Axis countries. So, my theory is that 'the Jew Strauss' was either a puppet in the hands of the German secret service or he was a Nazi agent himself."

Mr. Perl carefully wiped his lips with the corner of his napkin. Then he rubbed his fingers, one at a time, with lemon and dipped them in a finger bowl. He was visibly pleased with the rhythm he had managed to impose on his story and with the degree of interest he had managed to spark in me. Between us, a mess of empty lobster shells indicated that dinner was over. We left the restaurant, and to our surprise, it had begun to snow. Nothing serious, of course, just a few tentative flakes in the lines of fine, persistent rain. They melted before touching the earth.

"This snow won't stick, the radio just said so," announced the taxi driver who brought us back to the hotel. "Only up in the mountains. Years ago, there was more snow here, but nowadays it only snows on rare occasions. And around the shore it never sticks. No need to worry."

That driver got no tip. His blind belief in "what the radio says" had spoiled our childish hopes for a real blizzard.

The regulars had gathered back at the Illa D'Or bar, where the English drinkers talked of nothing but the unusual weather. A retired Scottish diplomat, thin as a telegraph pole, was regretting having spent half his life in Nordic and Canadian consulates; next to him, one of the grand old men of the colony—thirty years in a row, never missing a single winter—was bragging about that time he'd try to ski down one of the slopes of Puig Mallor. To celebrate the event, Mr. Costa decided to build a fire in the bar's fireplace and, as we entered, was announcing to his guests that the snowfall deserved a special cocktail. "I'm thinking of something really explosive. Something that I would put in the kegs of the Saint Bernards if I were the barman at a ski resort." The hotelier—who had been around the world a few times but pretended he'd never left his village—was having an inspired evening. As always, the Illa D'Or regulars applauded his creative efforts.

Meanwhile, comfortably sprawled in front of the fireplace, Mr. Perl and I continued our conversation. My curiosity centered on two points: what did "the Jew Strauss" really do, and what, exactly, was the Straperlo machine like?

"Strauss got his hooks into none other than Aureliano Lerroux, nephew and adopted son of Don Alejandro. With Aureliano as his paid advocate, he managed to navigate easily through the reefs and shoals of bureaucracy. Although gambling had been prohibited in Spain, Aureliano successfully argued that Straperlo was a game of calculation. Strauss never held back when it came to paying extremely generous commissions to ministers, executives, subsecretaries, functionaries, deputies, journalists; to the scrupulous he gave gold watches. Finally, the Home Office granted a provisional authorization for the Straperlo to be operated in the old San Sebastián casino, which, as you know, had a long and glittering history, but which had fallen into decay. Strauss bought it without even trying to negotiate the price and renovated it as quickly as he could, sparing no expense. Part of this huge investment came from high-risk credit acquired, God knows how, from Swiss and Dutch banks. Another part came from my father, or rather, from my mother's inheritance.

"The night the casino reopened, the grand salon glittered splendidly. Dozens of chandeliers illuminated the shiny Straperlo machines. Croupiers in full livery taught the rules of the new game to a large and glamorous public, so large, in fact, that it threatened to overwhelm the machines. Everything seemed to be moving along perfectly. Strauss was ecstatic. Even my mother was radiant and congratulated my father. Then suddenly, just three hours after the opening, with no prior warning, the police burst in with a warrant to close the place down. There were stampedes, panic, general hysteria..." Mr. Perl lapsed into silence.

Contrary to all prognostications, the snow did stick. It was no longer raining, and the thick flakes were falling with majestic slowness, transforming the conservatory that bordered the garden outside the bar into a spectacular Christmas card scene. As the evening's background music, Mr. Costa had chosen Schubert's *Die Winterreise*, perfectly in keeping with the strange atmosphere of broken dreams that had permeated our conversation. *Freund bin ich engezogen, Freund zieh ich wieder aus.* "I entered as a stranger, as a stranger I depart..." Mr. Costa had his points. There he was at the other end of the bar, surrounded by bottles and gadgets, completely engrossed in his alchemy, hoping, perhaps, to discover the true elixir of happiness.

Mr. Perl began again. "The San Sebastián business was a serious blow, but Strauss was not the kind who throws in the towel after the first setback. His friend, Aureliano Lerroux, swore again and again that it had all been a misunderstanding, that everything was under control. My father knew poor Adam Diehl, the owner of the Hotel Formentor, very well, and knew as well of his interest in building a grand casino on the tiny island at the mouth of the bay. They reached an agreement and, to begin, they restored a small building next to the hotel. The Straperlo machines ground into action again. Formentor seemed a more fitting place after all, because it was so far away, and because of the discreet, elite character of its clientele.

"The illusion lasted one week. On the eighth day, the police again invaded the place and sealed the machines. It seems it was Don Alejandro's own political allies in the government—the very ones who had accepted Strauss's bribes—who masterminded the operation to get rid of the old politician once and for all. Aureliano, his adopted son and Strauss's friend, was terrified to find the situation getting out of control, and hurriedly returned the 75,000 pesetas Strauss had advanced him. All of this coincided with the opening in Brussels of an international fair where Strauss and my father were presenting the Straperlo for the first time, with a view toward marketing it around the world. The situation was extremely delicate.

"Strauss began to maneuver desperately. He tried to juggle too many plates and ended up dropping all of them. Fleeing to the safety of the Hague, he sent a memorandum to Don Alejandro listing dates, sums, and the names of the numerous government functionaries implicated. He gave Don Alejandro a short amount of time to return, in one way or another, the 85,000 florins Strauss calculated as his investment up to that moment. Only then would he consider the matter closed; if Don Alejandro did not comply, Strauss would make the document public. In his memoirs, Don Alejandro recognizes that he was foolish in ignoring that letter, which was a real bomb. But his pride would not allow him to give in to what he considered a vulgar attempt at blackmail. Strauss's document finally reached the President of the Republic and the parties of the left. From there it leapt to Parliament and the press. The scandal exploded, acquiring hyperbolic proportions and eclipsing all other current affairs then in the news, including those of greater importance."

"Winter Journey!" announced Mr. Costa with a radiant expression on his face. "Winter Journey will be its name. I hope you like it." The new cocktail was an instant success. Everyone in the bar began guessing its ingredients. Coconut liqueur? Freezing, ice cold... Light rum? Cold, still chilly... Pisco? Getting warmer... Mr. Costa never revealed his secrets, but it was clear that exciting the curiosity of such seasoned drinkers pleased him immensely.

Winter Journey lived up to its name. It was a thick, unctuous cocktail, strong and sharp, of a strange ivory-white color quite appropriate to the thick mantle of snow which at that moment—by now it must have been about two o'clock in the morning—had settled over the entire island of Mallorca.

The snippets of news from outside were alarming. A taxi driver who worked the route from Palma to Formentor had to stop because of the condition of the highway. Both the driver and his fare had taken refuge in our hotel and were shaking off their chill next to the fireplace. They'd heard over the radio that the airport was closed. The driver himself had seen several electrical poles and many trees knocked down by the storm. People were warned to stay home if at all possible.

"My father never got over it." Mr. Perl took an old photograph out of his wallet and showed it to me. It was of a middle-aged man walking through the snow with a boy on his back.

"My mother took this shot of us around 1940, during a vacation we took in Bariloche, where we were invited by Ramón Ramouge. After escaping from Spain, he had returned to Argentina, and he thought my father might enjoy a visit to his boyhood home. But my father was no longer the same man. He was still young—born with the century—but he never pulled himself together. Not only because of the economic collapse, which was huge, but because something very profound had broken inside him, and he never managed to fix it. He became sour, dejected, and apathetic. He was suspicious of everyone. Nothing and no one deceived him ever again. My mother always said that the most painful thing for him had been the humiliation of being treated like a criminal. He believed blindly in his invention and considered himself the principal victim of Strauss's machinations. Seeing his name run from mouth to mouth as a synonym for swindle was torture for him. He forbade anyone to speak of it. He destroyed all the papers and documents related to the matter and tried to forget everything."

There was something disturbing and desolate in that faded photograph Mr. Perl showed me. Beyond the obvious physical resemblance between father and son, both figures shared something that I could not define, something like the same feeling of resignation, a kind of infinite fatigue that did not derive from the physical effort involved in walking through snow, something that had nothing to do with fatigue but spoke instead of the uncertainty or alienation of walking through life. I don't know why, but just then I remembered the woman who had been my teacher when I was a child. On the last day of class, just before summer vacation, she would always say, "Above all, children, don't forget that summer lasts three months, but winter lasts your entire life." And we would laugh. I was overtaken by a wave of tenderness, mixed with pity, for the man seated opposite me. If he ever did write his book, he should call it *In the Winter of My Father*. And then came another wave, tenderness flecked with the froth of admiration, for Mr. Costa, because his Winter Journey was the best damned drink I'd had in a long time. I managed to mumble, "Mr. Perl, once and for all, will you please explain to me what that fucking Straperlo game was like?"

"I don't have the slightest fucking idea, Mr. Rivas."

"For God's sake!"

It snowed all night and part of the next day. The radio announced it to be the greatest snowfall in Mallorca in the last thirty years.

Waking Up on the Floor

Alexandre Melo

No. I'm still in no condition to pose complicated questions. Where am I? How did I get here? It's very dangerous. I'm going to explain. Basic options. Would it be better to open my eyes or to move my head a bit? I shift my face slightly, from the side where my hair is a moist paste stuck to my skin and a hot, sultry fabric. I reek of sweat and dust, but now that my face is turned upward I feel a slight coolness. I part my cracked lips to exhale the sour, stale air inside my mouth and, with neither enthusiasm nor hope, run my dried-out tongue around it two or three times.

With one hand, I push my hair up off my head. That same slight coolness. I move my arm with surprising ease. Sooner or later, I will have to open my eyes. My head doesn't hurt much, at least as long as I don't try any more ambitious movements. I don't have to open my eyes to know that I am bathed in a convenient half-light. I don't think I took off my clothes, but it's too soon to check such details.

Yes. It's just what I thought. It could be worse. I'm on the floor. I turn my head again to one side, slowly, this time with my eyes open. The floor is covered by a dark, mouldy-smelling, chestnut-colored carpet. I'm going to take a deep breath and close my eyes for a little while before I look around again.

Unless someone objects, I'm going to stay like this, very quiet, until something happens or someone turns up. If I stay this way, nothing bad can happen to me. All the bad things in the world happen only because people don't stay at home, quiet, tranquil, stretched out in their own beds. No noises reach this place. There is silence, and this half-light is very fortunate.

But I can't prolong this immobility trick indefinitely. In any case, I won't be able to stop thinking about what happened to me yesterday—or what stopped happening to me yesterday. I should try to remember. It's better to go forward. I breathe out harder and lift my head, leaning on my right elbow, which slips on the rug.

I look to the right and behind and see a bed and a night table covered with things. My head hurts from the effort. I resume my original position, head straight, face up, eyes shut. I close a hand over my eyes until the dizziness passes. There was something else on the wall above the bed. I wipe the sweat away again and feel an unpleasant tightness in my throat. I run my tongue around my mouth a few more times, feeling my swollen gums.

Yes. It is a room. A bed. Why should I be on the floor instead of on the bed? Could I have been lying on the bed? And with whom? Who brought me here?

It's still very early to be thinking about all this. Very complicated.

A night table. Lots of things on top of it. A glass. I clearly saw a glass. My mania for having full glasses on the night table. Why does it have to be water? Now the thirst problem begins. I should have remembered it. Thirst.

One day, F. woke up with the usual desperate thirst and wanted iced water. The room was on the first floor, and the ice was in the bar, which was on the ground floor. We woke B. up to get ice. The stairway between the two floors of the apartment, the result of the renovation of an old property, was narrow and steep, with very shallow treads. In risky circumstances, the rule for going up or down was to hold on tight to the railing with both hands and walk slowly, one step at a time, holding one's head erect so as not to lose one's balance. I remember leaning my head against the railing before the last flight of steps. We heard a dense, muffled noise. We thought B. must have either forgotten the rule or forgotten to open his eyes. I went back to sleep. F. got tired of waiting and decided to drink the full glass I'd put on the night table before I went to bed. When I finally woke up, F. told me that the glass was full of gin, and laughed.

I always bring a glass of ice and gin to bed after a big night of drinking. It's a way of exorcising my fear of the night ending. A sublime illusion of the night without end. The fantasy of eternal alcohol. The comfort of satiety and the need to be able to count on something that will never end.

We found B. with no clothes on, sleeping on the white marble floor of the bar, illuminated by the marvelous glow of the light in the open refrigerator.

I am going to make an effort to open my eyes again. Perhaps it's worthwhile. I'll have to raise my head and slowly twist my neck around. Very slowly. The pearls are not really legitimate but the effect is the same. Pearls and perfume. They are a kind of idea.

R. talked non-stop, never missing the opportunity to use French terms, showing off with noisy pronunciation. R. preferred brand names in clothes and perfume, and dressed with disproportionate and provocative elegance. On the most formal evenings R. would flaunt a pearl necklace that could go around anyone's neck three times. The pearls were certainly artificial but served their purpose very well. That was how R. went out in the evenings, like everyone else at that time, but more exaggerated.

The pearls don't have only a decorative function.

One night, I managed to fill my mouth with all the pearls on the necklace after moistening them with iced vodka. It isn't easy. You move your mouth along little by little, taking in two or three pearls at a time. Your tongue, sweat, and skin help. But finally the loops get tangled up. To get some, you lose others. They crack against your teeth. My mouth full of pearls, I tried to unbutton R.'s shirt with my teeth. The first button finally yielded, but the pearls fell out. I moved on to the next button as R. started shouting. To save time, I pulled off the second button without trying to undo it. I stuffed R.'s mouth with the pearls to stop the shouting. R. spat them out on my head, which was moving downward. With my teeth, I pulled off another button, which came away with a tiny shred of cloth. It was the last one on the shirt. I knelt down to get to work on the trousers. R. grabbed the pearl necklace and began to scour my hair with it, shouting louder and louder, then whirled it up overhead like a lasso, whipping glasses out of the hands of nearby guests. I stood up in the midst of shattered glass to seize the necklace again. The pearl lasso began to rise again. There were more people shouting around us. Then two bouncers walked over, took me firmly, lifting me up over the heads on the dancefloor, and carried me out. A privileged perspective, on the shoulders of two musclemen, closing my eyes and letting my head fall back slightly, with nothing to hold onto. That total music. Meanwhile the pearls remained around R.'s neck.

They set me down out on the wide landing of the long flight of stone steps outside the door to the club. A few steps above me, P. was dozing, head bowed forward and hands tucked in shorts worn to show off long legs. P. wanted to be a model, and I thought about the common and persistent fantasy of being with models. I've got a knack for starting conversation, but I get really confused by the end of the evening. If the beginning of the conversation coincides with the end of the night, it's better not even to start. And the last thing I wanted to do was to start talking at that hour. P. stayed there dozing. I realized that I was still holding onto the handrail. I let go and stretched my fingers, then turned to go back inside. The music was still going on. I didn't find R.

And that's the very thing I'm going to do now. Stretch my fingers, arms, and legs. Unstick my ass from my clothes and the floor. Shake myself a bit. Loosen my tongue as much as possible. Take yet another look around. There's a telephone right here by my foot. A little closer, it could have been a pillow. But I'm still not prepared to think about making telephone calls.

R.M. liked to say that one should have one's bed in the living-room. V. would retort that one's living-room was one's bed.

Beds. There are the usual ways of keeping sheets fresh and stretched taut. But a bed can be a dangerous place. Whether before or after we do what we have to do, we don't go unpunished. Insomnia indicates a bad conscience. Guilt makes it difficult not to sleep alone. On the verge of suffocation, we reach the decision that it seems better to let oneself slip silently to the floor.

No. It does not have to be that way. This bed has a prosaic and welcoming air to it. Could it be I was lying there? Floral sheets have something touching and maternal about them. The fluffy pillow could have just been used. It makes me think of childhood. There is no doubt that my sensibility is very debilitated, but that will pass. A night table is a kind of grandmother's attic, but small. And later we discover that we no longer have a grandmother, and that the attic is our own.

My grandmother's house had no attic, but it did have two floors linked by a long staircase. Eight steps, a landing, four steps, another landing, and a final flight of fourteen steps. One of my favourite childhood games was to jump from the highest possible step and still manage to land on my feet. There were two ways to do it: hanging on and not hanging on. The safest way was to jump with one hand on the banister, which allowed for more balance while clearing more steps, and landing more solidly on the cold, hard, orange-colored mosaic floor. The family insisted that I not let go of the banister because if my foot slipped I could fall and break a bone. The bone I might have broken did not mean simply an arm or a leg but one of those terrible and definitive things that would involve a wheelchair for the rest of one's life. I got used to running the risk of a fracture. Sometimes I deliberately let myself fall onto the floor, just to feel the cold mosaic directly against my skin; to rub my bare, scraped knees against it or rest my forehead, flushed and sweaty from jumping, on the shiny tiles. When no one was looking, I would press my lips against the floor, letting my tongue savour the filthy, gelid taste that sent shivers through my whole body. Much later on, I remember watching my grandmother take an immense amount of time to walk up the stairs, holding onto the banister, moving her legs with difficulty.

…I always slept better in my room in my grandmother's house than in any other room, even though it faced a railroad line where trains constantly thundered past.

It's a matter of learning to sleep anywhere, through anything. But what rooms can be that way? The room in a provincial pension, where one arrives early in the afternoon and can't resist the temptation to have a siesta before taking a bath, changing clothes, and finding somewhere nice to have dinner. The room in a country house that one finds, year after year, exactly as if one had left it the night before, still with the mark of the body's weight on the mattress and pillow. They are kind of intermediary rooms that belong to no one but stand as if they have always been waiting for someone particular, possessing a familiarity as yet uncorrupted by the routines of use. They are suffused with the fears and unforseen things that are the raw materials of childhood fantasies and the more serious fantasies of adults. Threats and possibilities.

But all these are still real rooms, nothing more than the antechambers of the rooms that lie on the other side. Ideal places for dreams, rapes, and tortures. Neighborhoods full of knives and works of art. Improbable objects, enigmatic arrangements, secret sculptures, unfathomable ornaments. A bed is a stage, the base of the structure, made of columns, posts, crossbars, and ropes, where the images of bodies seen on the street, in films, and in magazines, swirl. Bodies invented to decorate the stage set of a theater in which I am author, director, and spectator of all the shows. I don't know if I'm also the protagonist.

Time is the sleep of God. Man becomes a fallen angel after falling and trying to get up. The angel that lets himself stay on the floor, fallen, is a ruined genius.

My sensibility is too fragile right now. I reached my memories of childhood and the mania about the conversations of angels too fast. I still have to deal with thirst and the telephone. That other matter has to be handled more slowly. Everyone has to hold onto something.

One night when I was coming home late I tripped over one of the stanchions they put on sidewalks to stop cars from parking there. To keep from falling, I grabbed onto the railing that separated the sidewalk from the street, but my hand slipped and I ended up cracking a tooth against the metal bar. It had no importance beyond the two hours I spent in the dentist's office and the guilty taste in my mouth.

Everyone has to hold onto something. I'm still not going to get up, not even move around. I'm going to leave the telephone alone. Rest, breathe, close my eyes, find courage.

I hear rapid footsteps approaching. The door opens behind me. I remain motionless. Someone comes towards me, then stops. I open my eyes.

"What are you going to do?"
"Don't worry. You won't be in the photograph."

About the Authors

John Berger is a writer, painter, critic, and storyteller whose most recent novel is *To the Wedding* (Pantheon). His other novels include *Pig Earth, Once in Europa, Lilac and Flag*, and *G.* (Vintage). He is the co-author, with Nella Bielski, of the play *Goya's Last Portrait*, and has written several books about art, including *Ways of Seeing, About Looking*, and *The Success and Failure of Picasso* (Vintage). He lives in France.

William Forsythe has been Artistic Director of the Ballett Frankfurt since 1984. His works include *The Vile Parody of Address, In the Middle, Somewhat Elevated, Limb's Theorem, The Loss of Small Detail, Alien/a(c)tion*, and *Eidos : Telos*. He lives in Frankfurt.

Dave Hickey is a writer of cultural criticism, fiction, and popular music. His books include *Prior Convictions*, a collection of short fiction (Southern Methodist University Press), and *The Invisible Dragon: Four Essays on Beauty* (Art Issues Press). He lives in Las Vegas, Nevada.

James Lingwood is a curator and writer, and is co-director of Artangel Trust in London. He has organised many contemporary and historical exhibitions throughout Europe, and was responsible for the exhibition of Juan Muñoz's work at the Irish Museum of Modern Art in 1994. He lives in London.

Alfred MacAdam has translated the works of Carlos Fuentes and Fernando Pessoa among many other Hispanic writers. He is professor of Latin American literature at Barnard College/Columbia University, and is literary critic and editor of *Review: Latin American Literature and Arts* (The Americas Society). He lives in New York.

Partick McCabe is the author of several novels, including *The Butcher Boy* (Delta), *The Dead School* (Dial), and a play, *Frank Pig Says Hello*. A film of *The Butcher Boy* is to be directed by Neil Jordan. He lives in Dublin.

Alexandre Melo is an art critic and teaches sociology of culture at the University of Lisbon. His most recent book is *Velocidades Contemporaneas* (Assirio and Alvím). He lives in Lisbon.

Vik Muniz is an artist and writer who lives and works in New York. He is also the Associate Editor of *Blind Spot Magazine.*

Juan Muñoz's first solo exhibition took place in 1984 at the Galeria Fernando Vijande in Madrid; since then he has exhibited extensively throughout Europe and the United States. A volume of his own writings, *Segment* (Centre d'Art Contemporain, Geneva, and The Renaissance Society of Chicago), was published in 1990. He lives in Madrid.

Louise Neri is U.S. Editor of *Parkett Magazine*. She is also Project Associate at Artangel Trust in London, and co-curator of the 1997 Whitney Biennial at the Whitney Museum of American Art. She lives in New York.

Quico Rivas is a writer and curator. He lives in the Canary Islands.

Luc Sante is the author of *Low Life* (Vintage) and *Evidence* (Farrar, Straus and Giroux), and is the photography critic of *The New Republic*. He lives in Brooklyn.

Adrian Searle is an artist, writer and curator. He is the art critic of *The Guardian,* and a regular contributor to *Time Out* and *Frieze*. He lives in London.

Lynne Tillman is the author of *Haunted Houses, Absence Makes the Heart, Motion Sickness, Cast in Doubt* (Serpent's Tail), and *The Madame Realism Complex* (Semiotexte). She also wrote the text for *The Velvet Years,* a book of Stephen Shore's photographs of Andy Warhol and the Factory, 1965 – 1967 (Pavilion Press). She lives in New York.

Marina Warner's fiction includes the novels *The Lost Father* and *Indigo,* and a collection of short stories, *The Mermaids in the Basement* (Vintage). She has also written several volumes of cultural criticism, including a series of lectures, *Six Myths of Our Time* (Random House), and a study of fairy tales, *From the Beast to the Blonde* (Farrar, Straus and Giroux). She lives in London.